physics for the design arts

Richard D. Haracz

To order books or for customer service, please call 1(800)-CALL-WILEY (225-5945).

Printed in the United States of America.

ISBN 978- 0-471-77703-8

10 9 8 7 6 5 4 3

Contents

Chapter 10. Optics

Chapter 11. The Wave Nature of Light

Chapter 12. Electricity

Chapter 13. Electric Circuits and Ohm's Law

Chapter 14. The Magnetic Field and Electromagnetism

Chapter 15. The Worldview Changes – Special Relativity

Chapter 16. The Worldview Changes – Quantum Mechanics

Appendix

PART 1

Mechanics, Thermodynamics, & Waves

Introduction to the First Course

1.	What is Real?

We will begin with an assumption. There is something real out there. It not all a dream in the sense of "The Matrix." We assume that we are not wired to a massive computer system and fed with a perception of what the system lords want us to regard as real. Of course, this is an assumption. We assume that there is a reality that interacts with us through our senses. We accept the input messages, assimilate and interpret these signals in our own special way as scientists or artists, and we create the known universe as it fits our receptions of the real thing. Needless to say, the known universe continually changes as we mature, just as the world to a child changes with age.

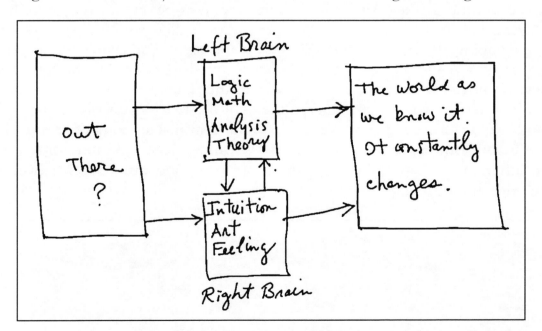

"Out There" is the real reality. We assume that it exists. Humans perceive this reality through the senses or by observations — experiments- that extend the senses. The impulses received by a person are analyzed, and both sides of the brain make interpretations. The left side applies the rules of logic and mathematics, and the right side uses intuition and whatever else the social environment offers to interpret the impulses from the real thing. The result is "the world as we know it." The question that has been asked since Plato is what can be trust as knowledge about the known world? Some believe that only the senses and logical analysis give reliable information about reality. Others believe that the mind and the complex internal thinking processes, including artistic and literary intuition, results in knowledge that does mirror reality. In this course, the physicist and design artist will have a chance to argue the point, but the material under discussion will be the principles of physics as discovered by the physics community since Isaac Newton.

Sarah Stolfa, a student from last year's class and a recent graduate from Drexel University, in a professional photographer whose course project on the theme "Alternate Realities" appears below. If you study the images carefully, they will become somewhat unsettling — there is something strange about the man on the left and on the right. The center photo is a picture of a man at a bar — it is in fact a noted work by Ms. Stolfa. She digitally moved the eyes of the man so that the frame on the left is his face with two left eyes, and the frame on the right has two right eyes together. If you look at the eyes, they make the left and right images somewhat unreal. We know from experience that no one is symmetrical. Left and right eyes are different, perhaps mimicking the more profound differences between the sides of our brain.

2.   The Limitations of Physics

The way we perceive what is out there comes to us through our senses. In science, the senses are greatly augmented by experimental devises, such as the microscope, telescope, electronic devices and the computer. As the technology for measurement are refined and enlarged by technological advancement, the range of perception increases, and our view of reality in enhanced and refined. This means that the world as we define it changes as the means to observe it improves, and these changes spawn new ways to observe.

Newton's physics is discussed in the first course. However, the tools to observe were limited in the seventeenth century, and it turns out that many of the fundamental assumptions about space, time and forces were incorrect. The interpretation of the experiments of the classical era, though highly accurate and extremely useful, built a "world as we know it" that has raised our standard of living and spawned marvels of engineering and science. The experiments, or sensory information, used by Newton and the classical physicists, were not wrong – they were simplistic and sometimes wrongly interpreted. So, even the world of the scientist constructed with great care and faithful adherence to the available evidence can be wrong, illusionary and changeable.

There are also limitations[1] on knowledge that is based on current and up to date experiments and fully accepted principles of physics and mathematics. For example, three great thinkers of the twentieth century revealed limitations about reality that are universally accepted. Albert Einstein in his special theory of relativity[2] (1905) showed that the speed of light is constant no matter how this speed is measured, and the value is c = 3×10^8 m/s. Moreover, the speed of light is a limiting speed for all matter – nothing can travel faster than the speed c. Another part of this package is that objects cannot travel backward in time without violating a principle of cause and effect.

---

[1] Palle Yourgrau in "A World Without Time (Basic Book, 2005) discusses the relationship between Albert Einstein and Kurt Gödel and the limitations of formal rational thought. The premise of the book is that Gödel presents solutions of Einstein's equations of general relativity that call in to question the existence of time as a fundamental parameter.
[2] The original work is in Annalen der Physik, vol. 17, 1905 on page 841.

Werner Heisenberg[3] (1927) showed that the measurement of the momentum of a particle (related to speed) and its position cannot both be measured with certainty- if one is measured exactly, the other can have any value. This means that there is a necessary incompleteness about what we can know exactly concerning the parameters of the physical world.

Kert Gödel[4] (1931) proved that a complete set of true mathematical statements can never achieved by any formal mathematical system. That is, any formal system may contain propositions that are true intuitively, but they cannot establish as true or false by the formal structure. A formal system is one containing axioms involving defined objects, rules for manipulating these objects, and the objects have no meaning outside their definitions in the system. If it is assumed that a machine is a formal system, and that a computer program is a machine in this sense, then Gödel's incompleteness theorem is a fundamental limitation on what a machine, like a computer, can do.

Art, however, does not have play this game and does not have to abide by the rules of logic, experimental facts or the laws of physics. We see in film and literature scenarios were human space travelers move faster than the speed of light. We see time travel to the past and the future. We see paintings in which impossible realizations are placed together existing quite comfortably on the canvas. Moreover, some of the most fascinating science fiction presents us with artificial intelligences - robots and computers and the like – that are at least the equal of human beings and not limited in any way. So, can a freewheeling and widely imaginative artistic creation provide unique and meaningful insights about what really is? This question has been asked since the time of Plato, and it is still the one of the most beguiling of puzzles. This course asks you to take a stab at an answer, but you are also asked to seek an appreciation of the power of the scientific method and physics in understanding and coping with challenges of the sensible world

So, what is our job in this course?

- First and foremost, this is a physics course. The laws of physics, starting with Newton and moving through quantum mechanics will be presented. The treatment will be algebra based, equations presented. Examples will be given throughout the text, homework will be assigned and graded and tests will occur regularly. These will be used to determine part of your course grade.

---

[3] The uncertainty principle first appears in Werner Heisenberg in Zeitschrift fur Physik, vol. 43, 1927, pages 172-198.
[4] The incompleteness theory was formulated by Kurt Gödel in 1931 in Monatschefte fur Mathematik and Physik, vol. 38, pages 173-198.

- Your artistic interpretation of the physics principles will be sought and added to the mix of the course. Projects will be assigned to express and communicate your reactions, and you will use the tools of your design discipline in this process. For example, course projects in all the design disciples have interpreted such themes as "Space and Time in Art," The Arrow of Time," Uncertainly in Art" and "Alternate Realities." As we move through the course together, we will always pause to explore how imagination and artistic freedom can reflect these laws either faithfully or challenge them. These projects will also be used to determine your course grade.
- The appendix for our two courses contains twelve sample projects created by students in the Fall Quarter of 2004 and Winter or 2005.

---

3.   Introduction to the first course

Physics provides one way to view reality. It does this by defining possible way of looking at reality that can be verified in a repeatable way by measurements. Space is the medium into which physical objects exist in definite positions, and these positions can change. Change is measured by a parameter called time.

The connection of the concepts of space and time to measurement is accomplished by defining units of measurement, for example the distance of something from a reference location is expressed in terms of meters or feet, and the passage of time (change) is measured in seconds.

The laws of physics relate the fundamental concepts of space and time to composite concepts such as speed and acceleration. Matter is of course a central player in the description of reality, and it is quantified by the concept of mass. Newton's laws of motion express how these parameters change in time from an initial point in time, and the picture that emerges from what is called the classical model for reality. The description of motion of massive objects interacting with each other is called **Mechanics**.

Mechanics can also be described in a complementary way by introducing the idea of energy, and the mechanical energy then points to the need for another kind of energy called heat. The changes and relationships that involve heat energy, measured by temperature, are lead to a set of physical laws called the laws of thermodynamics, and these add an interesting slant to Newton's laws and time. The equations of mechanics predict a universe that can run backward in time as easily as forward. The second law of thermodynamics tells us that there is a direction to time – an arrow of time – so that clocks runs toward the future and all things tend to age.

These topics are called "classical physics" because they the span a period of over three hundred years since Sir Isaac Newton lived and worked. The classical era extends to the beginning of the twentieth century.

The classical era took a different turn in the eighteenth and nineteenth centuries with electricity and magnetism and the concept of a "wave field" that fills space. We will begin the discussion of waves this term and carry it forward next term.

The course lectures are presented using the Tablet PC technology. I am able to draw and write on the screen while you watch and take notes. These drawing and hand-written explanations are given here. As artists, you can appreciate the usefulness of drawings as they somewhat reflect the personality of the drawer. As a physicist, and an entrenched left-brain person, these drawings should give you a chuckle.

CHAPTER 1

Newton's Concept of Space and Time

1. Who Was Newton?

Isaac Newton[5] did not invent the science of Physics; perhaps the starting point is closer to Galileo Galilei. However, his impact on the human condition was immense. Michael Hunt in "The 100" (London, citadel Press, 1992)[6] makes this assertion that the 100 most influential people in history include Isaac Newton in second place – behind Muhammad and just before Jesus. This evaluation, naturally the opinion of Mr. Hunt, is based on Newton's influence in molding modern thought since about 1670 and extending to the present.

- He quantified scientific methodology including the concepts of space, time, force and motion, gravity and the precise motion of the planets and optics. He also invented the differential calculus to express his ideas, along with Gottfried von Leibniz.

- To balance this, he was also the premier alchemist of his time, and his library on the subject may be the largest and most compete ever established. He clearly did not want to leave out any avenue to understanding the universe.

---

[5] Isaac Newton was born in 1643, one year after the death of Galileo. He published "The Mathematical Principles of Natural Philosophy in 1687, and it represented at least twenty years of work in which he pioneer the fields of optics, invented the differential calculus, the laws of motion and universal gravitation. It so doing, he establishes a worldview that we happy use today. This work appears in its entirety in a beautiful collection called "On the Shoulders of Giants by Stephen Hawing, Running Press, 2002.

[6] This reference appears in the book "Isaac Newton – the Last Sorcerer" by Michael White (Addison Wesley, 1997). It appears that Newton was indeed an outstanding Alchemist with a world-class library on this subject. Newton did not leave out any option.

As we will see, the physics of Newton has been revised fundamentally, but his model of space, time and motion still proves to be extremely accurate and useful in our building of the tools and structures of our civilization. So, the first systematic model of reality beyond the age of magic, the way we picture the world, is a direct derivative of Newtonian physics. This model will occupy us for most of the both courses.

2.   Thinking things through – the scientific method

One characteristic of Science is the use of Aristotelian logic. Let's do a thought problem to illustrate how a scientist, or problem solver like Isaac Newton or a left-brain consulting detective such as Sherlock Holmes, confront a mystery.

Problem Statement: How many piano tuners are in Philadelphia?

Data: Population is 1.5 million people. Average size of a family = 2.5.

Assumptions: 1/3 of the families have pianos.

Average time between tunings = 10 years

A tuner can do 4 instruments per day over 250 days a year.

Solution:

number of pianos in Phila → 1.5×10^6 people $\frac{family}{2.5 \, people}$ $\frac{1}{3}$ $\frac{Pianos}{Family}$

$= 200,000$ pianos

Pianos tuned/year $= \dfrac{200,000 \, pianos}{10 \, years} = 20,000$ Pianos/year

Pianos / tuner $= 4 \times 250 = 1000$

tuners needed $= \dfrac{20,000 \, pianos/year}{1000 \, pianos/tuner} = 20 \, tuners$

3.   The parameters of space and time as scalar quantities and their units

Newton assumed that space and time are absolute quantities into which material things are placed. He also assumed that space and time are separate and distinct. Both of these assumptions, though carrying the force of common sense, are wrong, but the story as we will now tell it will carry forward this unrealistic view.

The basic parameters of distance and time are expressed as real numbers, and these numbers are attached by comparison to arbitrary standards. Quantities so expressed in terms of real numbers are called **Scalar Quantities.**

a) Length.

Given two points in space, we called distance the length of the straight line that connects these points. The length can be expressed anyway your want, like the number of foot lengths needed to pace off this distance. Clearly, in order that the idea to be useful to more that one person, a standard length is required which all will agree to use. In this course, we will use the standard used throughout the world. It is called the international standard. But to emphasize the arbitrary nature of standards, another will be used which is called the engineering system. The United States uses this in most of its engineering projects. We start with two points A and B and a straight line drawn between them:

```
                origin
            ┌──┴──────────┬────────────────────►
            0             L                      x

L = standard length
International   1 meter (m)
Engineering     1 foot (ft)
        1 centimeter (cm) = 10⁻² m          1 kilometer = 1100 m
        1 millimeter (mm) = 10⁻³ m
        1 micrometer (μm) = 10⁻⁶ m
        1 nanometer (nm) = 10⁻⁹ m
        1 yard = 3 ft
        1 mile = 5,280 ft                  1 inch = ft · 1/12
        1 furlong = 1/8 mile
Conversion      1 m = 3.281 ft
                    = 3.281 ft (1 yard)/(3 ft) = 1.094 yds
```

b) Time.

Time expresses the notion of change. An object can be in one location and then move to another location. The change can be abrupt or gradual, as we perceive it, and therein lay the notion of time. We perceive the length of the duration of day and light to be regular and predictable, so it is not surprising that our concept of duration or time follows the Earth. The unit in all systems is the second:

```
unit = 1 second (s)        heartbeat
1 minute = 60 s
1 hour = 60 min = 60 min (60s)/(1 min) = 3600 s
1 day = 24 hours = 24 hours (3600s)/(hr) = 86,400 s
1 week = 7 d
1 year = 365 d = 365 d (86,400 s)/(d) = 3.15×10⁷ s
1 fortnight = 14 days
```

4. Mass - Quantity of Matter.

Space is the medium for things in the physical world. Objects are set at locations and their locations can change in time. But what are these objects? With the exception of light, they are characterized by a quantity of matter, which is related to their weight on the Earth's surface. The standard for this idea is an actual piece of platinum and Iridium kept safely near Paris. The unit of "mass" of this is called the Kilogram, abbreviated kg. Mass is actually independent of the existence of the Earth and gravity, but we will make this distinction later.

$$
\boxed{\text{Standard}} \quad 1 \text{ kilogram } (kg)
$$

$$
1 \text{ metric ton} = 2000 \text{ kg}
$$

$$
1 \text{ gram } (g) = 10^{-3} \text{ kg}
$$

Conversion

$$
1 \text{ kg weighs } 2.2 \text{ pounds on the surface of the earth}
$$

5. Derived units and systems of units.

a) Speed

This is the concept of motion which we will discuss in the next chapter. It combines space and time as:

$$\text{Speed} = \frac{\text{distance}}{\text{time}} = m/s \quad \text{meters per second}$$

$$1 \text{ mile/hour} = 1 mph = \frac{5,280 \text{ ft}}{\text{hour}} \frac{\text{hour}}{3600 \text{ s}} = 1.47 \text{ ft/s}$$

$$= \frac{5,280 \text{ ft}}{hr} \frac{1 m}{3.281 \text{ ft}} = 1.61 \times 10^3 m/hr$$

$$= 1.61 \text{ km/hr}$$

$$1 \text{ km/hr} = \frac{1}{1.61} = 0.62 \text{ mph}$$

b) Conversion of units and examples

$$v = 60 \text{ miles/hr} = \boxed{60 \text{ mph}}$$

$$= 60 \frac{\text{miles}}{hr} \left(\frac{1 m}{3.281 \text{ ft}}\right)\left(\frac{5,280 \text{ ft}}{1 \text{ mile}}\right)\left(\frac{1 \text{ km}}{1000 m}\right)$$

$$= \boxed{96.6 \text{ km/hr}}$$

$$= 96.6 \frac{\text{km}}{hr} \left(\frac{1 hr}{3600 s}\right)\left(\frac{1000 m}{1 \text{ km}}\right) = \boxed{26.8 m/s}$$

$$v = \frac{1 \text{ furlong}}{\text{fortnight}} = \frac{1 \text{ furlong}}{\text{fortnight}} \left(\frac{1/8 \text{ mile}}{\text{fortnight}}\right)\left(\frac{1 \text{ fortnight}}{14 d}\right) = 8.929 \times 10^{-3} \text{ miles/d}$$

$$= 8.929 \times 10^{-3} \frac{mi}{d} \left(\frac{5,280 \text{ ft}}{mi}\right)\left(\frac{1 d}{86400 s}\right)\left(\frac{12 in}{1 ft}\right)$$

$$= 6.55 \times 10^{-3} \text{ in/s}$$

6.   One-Dimensional Coordinate Systems

We now come to an important concept in expressing the idea of space and motion that is quantifiable and the foundation of physical laws or equations of motion. A coordinate system can describe by a space of any dimension- one, two, three (space as we know it) or more. It is sensible to start with one dimension. It is represented by a directed straight line called the x axis with a starting point called the origin, and tic marks indicating the unit of length.

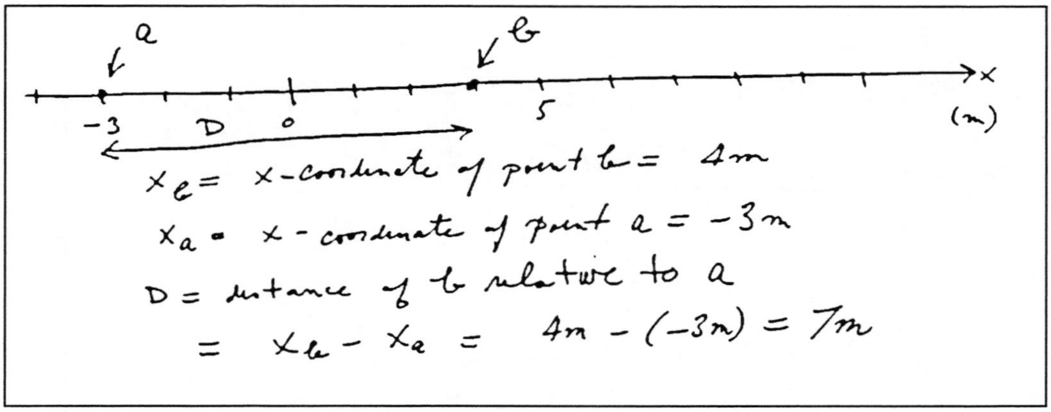

$x_b = $ x-coordinate of point $b = 4m$

$x_a = $ x-coordinate of point $a = -3m$

$D = $ distance of b relative to a

$\quad = x_b - x_a = 4m - (-3m) = 7m$

7.   Two-dimensional coordinate systems

Two dimensions are depicted by two directed lines at right angles to each other, intersecting at a point called the origin. Again, marks are placed along each line to indicate the unit of length, and the axes are called x and y.

a) Coordinate Axes.

Two points a and b are drawn below – one on the negative x axis and the other in the first quadrant (counterclockwise from upper right around to lower left). The distance between these points is then calculated using some geometry and the Pythagorean theorem:

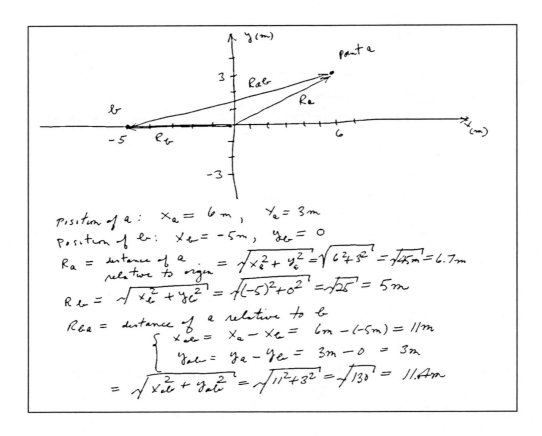

b) Vectors.

The example just completed has directed lines to depict the positions of the two points and the distance of the second point b from the point a. Just directed lines are called vectors:

vector = a quantity that has magnitude and direction (an arrow)

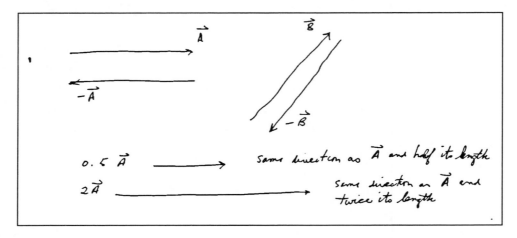

> ## 8. Vector Arithmetic.

We know how to deal with real numbers, scalars. We can add, subtract, multiple and divide them. Vectors can also be manipulated

a) Addition and subtraction.

We will define this process by examples.

- Example 1. Addition

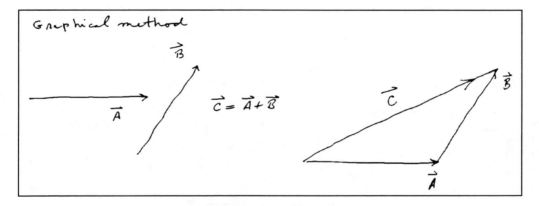

- Example 2. Addition and Subtraction

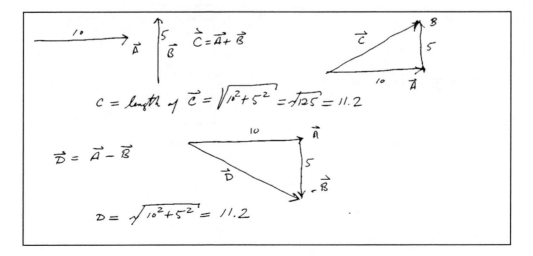

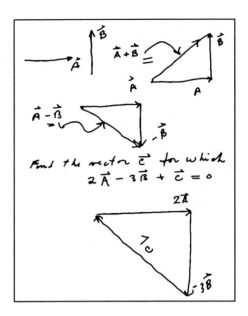

- Example 3. A problem using vectors for a map distances.

A trip : starting at 0, a car travels 10 miles due East. It then travels 5 miles due North, and finally 15 miles due West. How far from the origin does it travel ?

$\vec{D}$ = vector distance traveled from O

$$x_D = -5 \, mi \quad , \quad y_D = 5 \, mi$$

$$D = \text{distance} = \sqrt{(-5)^2 + 5^2} = \sqrt{50} = 7.07 \, miles$$

b) Multiplication of by a scalar.

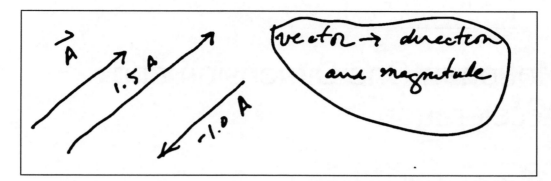

Motion in One Dimension and Acceleration

1.	Motion in one dimension.

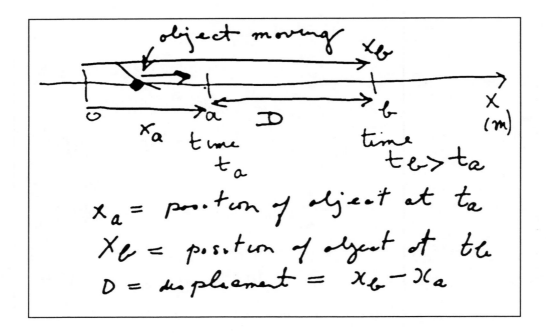

a) Average velocity

   As an an object as it moves between two positions, we define

   v (average) = displacement/ time interval = $(x_b - x_a)/(t_b - t_a) = \Delta x / \Delta t$ unit of average velocity = m/s

   Note that Δx = vel x change in time.

- Example: In 1989, Ann Thomson broke the US record for a 24 hour run by covering 143 miles. What was her average velocity expressed in ft/s?

$$v_{ave} = \frac{\Delta x}{\Delta t} = \frac{143 \text{ miles}}{24 \text{ hours}} = 5.96 \text{ m/h}$$

$$= 5.96 \frac{\text{miles}}{\text{hr}} \left(\frac{5281 \text{ ft}}{\text{mile}} \right) \frac{\text{hr}}{3600 \text{ s}}$$

$$= 8.7 \text{ ft/s}$$

b) Instantaneous velocity

v(instantaneous) = v = limit as $\Delta t \rightarrow 0$ of the ratio $(\Delta x / \Delta t)$
                    v = dx/dt (the differential of x with respect to t)

This is the essence of the differential calculus invented by Newton and Liebnez.

- **The speedometer of your car reads the instantaneous velocity.**

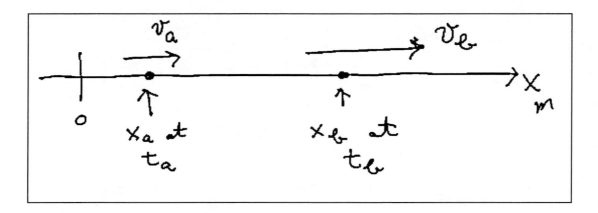

c) Average acceleration

As an object moves between positions x_a and x_b its average accelerations is

$$a(average) = (vb - va) / (tb - ta) = \Delta v / \Delta t$$
$$unit = (m/s)/s = m/s^2$$

note: Δv = change in velocity = a(average) x change in time.

- Example: A car is stopped at a light. When the light turns green, the car accelerates so that it is going 15 m/s after 5 seconds. What is the average acceleration of the car?

$$a_{ave} = \frac{v_{final} - v_{initial}}{time\ interval}$$
$$= \frac{15\ m/s - 0}{5\ s} = 3\ m/s^2$$

Suppose that the car now moves in the negative x direction at −10 m/s and the brakes are applied bringing it to rest with an average acceleration of 5 m/s². How long does it take to come to rest?

$$a_{ave} = 5\ m/s^2 = \frac{v_{final} - v_{initial}}{time\ interval} = \frac{0 - (-10\ m/s^2)}{t}$$
$$5 = \frac{10}{t} \rightarrow t = \frac{10}{5} = 2t$$

$$v_f = 0 \qquad a = 5\ m/s^2 \rightarrow \qquad v_i = -10\ u/s \leftarrow$$

d) Instantaneous acceleration.

a (instantaneous) = a = limit as $\Delta t \to 0$ of the ratio $(\Delta v / \Delta t)$

a = limit (as $\Delta t \to 0$) $(\Delta v / \Delta t)$ = dv/dt
    = the derivative of velocity with respect to time

2.	Equations of motion by example.

a) Free-Fall.

Using the definitions given in the last section, we will write equations relating space (the x coordinate) and time (t). Remember that Newton assumed that space and time are absolute and independent of each other, but motion combines them as parameters in what are called equations of motion.

An equation of motion relates space (x) and time (t) and describes the motion of an object. Free fall is the situation where the only force acting on the object is gravity. As the result of this force, the object accelerates toward the ground (center of the Earth) with a constant acceleration of a = g = 9.8 m/s

$$v_{ave} = \frac{x_b - x_a}{t_b - t_a} = \frac{\Delta x}{\Delta t}$$

$$v = \lim_{\Delta t \to 0} \Delta x / \Delta t \quad \left(\text{speedometer reading} \right)$$

$$a_{ave} = \frac{v_b - v_a}{t_b - t_a} = \frac{\Delta v}{\Delta t}$$

$$a = \lim_{\Delta t \to 0} \frac{\Delta v}{\Delta t}$$

As an example, consider a ball is thrown upward at a speed of 20 m/s. The acceleration of gravity is 10 m/s^2 downward. The ball rises to its maximum height and then descends. How long does the ball take to reach a speed of 10 m/s downward?

$$a = -10 \, m/s^2 \; (9.8)$$

downward _away_

$$a = \frac{v_b - v_a}{t_b - t_a}$$

$$-10 \, \frac{m}{s^2} = \frac{-10 \, m/s - 20 \, m/s}{t}$$

$$t = \frac{-30 \, m/s}{-10 \, m/s^2} = 3 \, sec$$

How long does it take for the same ball to move to the top of its trajectory, noting that at the top the velocity is zero instantaneously?

$$a = -g = -10 \, m/s^2$$

$$-10 \, m/s^2 = \frac{v_a - v_a}{t_b - t_a}$$

$$= \frac{0 - 20 \, m/s}{t}$$

$$t = \frac{-20}{-10} = 2 \, sec$$

b) One-dimensional motion with a constant velocity.

We can use the definition of constant velocity to develop an equation of motion relating distance and time.

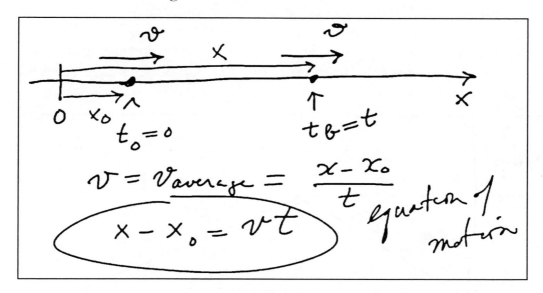

$$v = v_{average} = \frac{x - x_0}{t} \quad \text{equation of motion}$$

$$\boxed{x - x_0 = vt}$$

The graphical representation of this motion follows:

$$x - x_0 = vt \quad \text{or} \quad x = x_0 + vt$$
$$v = \text{velocity} > 0$$

straight line

Slope $\equiv \dfrac{\Delta x}{\Delta t} = $ velocity

Ex: $x_0 = 2m$ and $v = 5 m/s$

$x = 2m + 5 m/s \; t$ ✓

The position at $t = 10 sec$ is $\rightarrow 52 m$

How long does it take for the object t_0 move $100 m$?

$$100 m = 2m + 5 m/s \; t \rightarrow \left(\frac{100-2}{5}\right) sec$$

An example of an equation of motion for constant velocity

A car moves with a constant velocity, v = 50 miles/hour. It passes the origin (x=0) at time t = 0 in the positive x direction, and travels a distance of 25 miles. The car then moves back to the origin at a constant speed v' and returns when the time is t = 1.5 hours, measured from the start of the journey. Two things are desired: the x versus t curve for the round trip and how long does it take for the car to travel from x = 0 to x=25 miles?

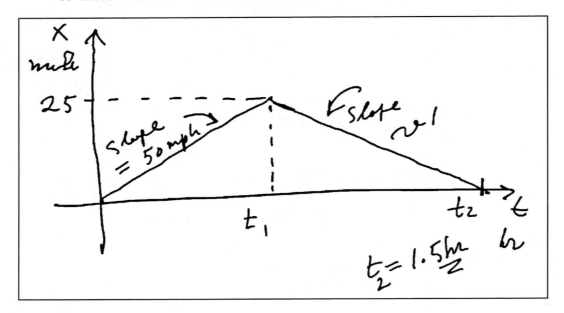

$$x = vt$$

$$x = 50 \frac{miles}{hr} t$$

$$x = 25 \; mile = \frac{50 \; miles}{hr} t$$

$$t = 25 \; miles / 50 \; miles/hr = 0.5h$$

Now let's find the velocity during the return trip to the origin?

$$x_2 - x_1 = v'(t_2 - t_1)$$

$$0 - 25 \, mi/hr = v'(1.5 hr - 0.5 hr)$$

$$-25 \, mi/hr = v' / hour$$

$$v' = \frac{-25 \, mi/hr}{1 hr.} = \boxed{-25 \, mph}$$

---

3.   Motion in one-dimensional with constant acceleration

This is a special case of motion that is useful to analyze. It leads to equations of motion that are linear and apply to the motion of objects that move above the surface of the Earth under the influence of gravity. We will first approach this case graphically.

a) Graphical representation.

$$v = constant \qquad x - x_0 = vt$$

$$x = x_0 + vt$$

slope $= v$

x_0 $t_0 = 0$

Note $x_0 < 0$

$$\boxed{x = x_0 + vt}$$

when is $x = 0$:

$$0 = x_0 + vt \Rightarrow t = -\frac{x_0}{v} > 0$$

b) Constant acceleration.

When the acceleration is constant, average acceleration equals instantaneous acceleration, and

$$a(average) = a = (v - v_0)/(t - t_0) = (v - v_0)/t, \quad t_0 = 0,$$

where "0" stands for the initial. That is v_0 is the velocity at time $t_0 = 0$, and v is the velocity at time t. If we solve for the velocity, we then get

$$v = v_0 + at.$$

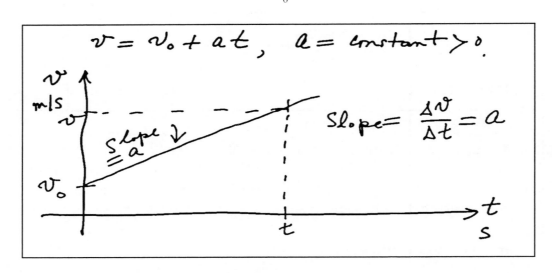

- x versus time.

The velocity is not constant when the acceleration is nonzero, but the average velocity over the time interval $0 \rightarrow t$ is

$$v(average) = (v + v_0)/2 = (x - x_0)/t$$

We can re-organized this equation as follows:

$$\frac{v + v_0}{2} = \frac{x - x_0}{t} \rightarrow x - x_0 = \frac{v + v_0}{2} t$$

$$x - x_0 = \frac{vt}{2} + \frac{v_0 t}{2} \checkmark$$

$$v = v_0 + at \checkmark$$

$$x - x_0 = \frac{(v_0 + at)}{2} t + \frac{v_0 t}{2} = \frac{v_0 t}{2} + \frac{1}{2} a t^2 + \frac{v_0 t}{2}$$

$$\boxed{x - x_0 = v_0 t + \frac{1}{2} a t^2}$$

equation of motion for $a = \text{constant}$

This is the equation of motion (space versus time) when the acceleration a is constant.

- A plot of the equation of motion for constant acceleration.

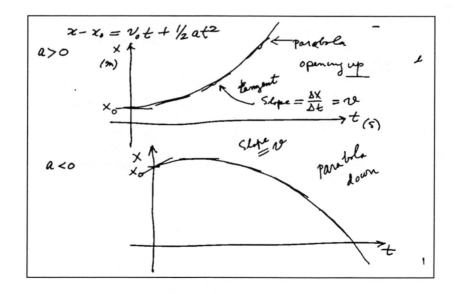

The curve drawn above is a parabola. If a is positive, the parabola opens upward; if a is negative the parabola opens downward. Consider graphically a situation in which an object moves along the positive x axis with a constant positive acceleration a, then it moves with a with a negative acceleration a':

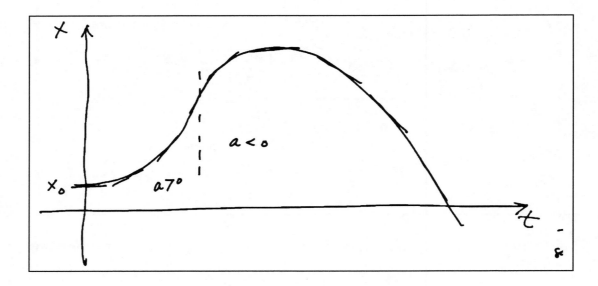

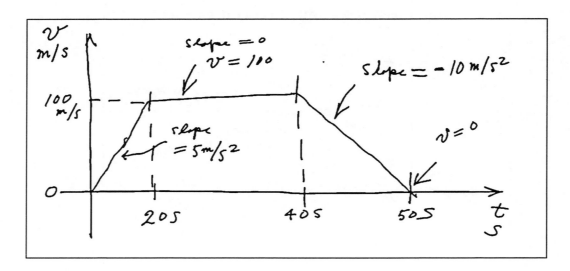

c) Example:

A car starts from rest at t = 0 at the origin xo = 0, and it accelerates at a constant value of a = 5 m/s² for 20 seconds. It then moves with the speed attained at t = 20 seconds for another 20 seconds, and finally the car brakes to rest in 10 seconds. We first draw a curve for v versus time for the entire event.

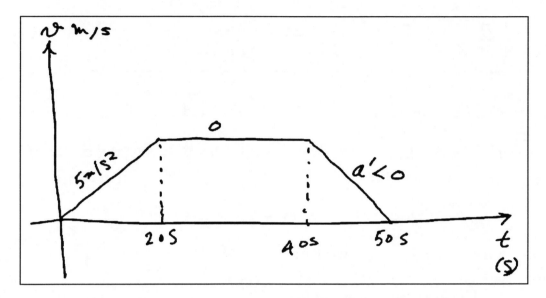

What is the total length that the car moves?

$0 \rightarrow 20S$ $\quad x - x_0 = v_0 t + \frac{1}{2} a t^2$

$\qquad x = 0 + \frac{1}{2} 5 m/s^2 (20 s)^2 = \boxed{1000\ m}$

$\qquad v - v_0 = a t \rightarrow v = 5 m/s^2 (20 s) = 100 m/s$

$20 \rightarrow 40 S$ $\quad x - x_0 = v_0 t = 100 m/s (20 s) = \boxed{2000\ m}$

$40 \rightarrow 50 S$ $\quad v - v_0 = a' t \rightarrow 0 - 100 m/s = a' 10 S$

$\qquad a' = -10 m/s^2$

$\qquad x - x_0 = v_0 t + \frac{1}{2} a' t^2 = 100 (10) + \frac{1}{2}(-10)(10)^2$

$\qquad\qquad = 1000 m - 500 m = \boxed{500\ m}$

Total $\Delta x = 1000 + 2000 + 500 = 3500\ m$

What is the average velocity and average acceleration over the full range?

$$V_{ave} = \frac{\Delta X}{\Delta t} = \frac{3500m}{50\,s} = 70\ m/s$$

$$a_{ave} = \frac{\Delta v}{\Delta t} = \frac{0-0}{50\,s} = 0$$

d) Freefall again using equations of motion and examples

The acceleration due to gravity is downward toward the center of the earth and it has the constant value

$$a = -9.8\ \text{m/s}^2 = -32.2\ \text{ft/s}^2,$$

where the minus sign indicates the −y or downward direction.

- The equations of motion:

$$a = -g = -10\ m/s^2$$

$$y - y_0 = v_0 t + \frac{1}{2}(-10 m/s^2)\, t^2$$
$$= v_0 t - 5 m/s^2\, t^2$$

$$v - v_0 = -gt = -10 m/s^2\, t$$

- Example 1. A well is so deep that you cannot see to the bottom, so you drop a stone into the well and hear the splash 10 seconds later. How deep is the well?

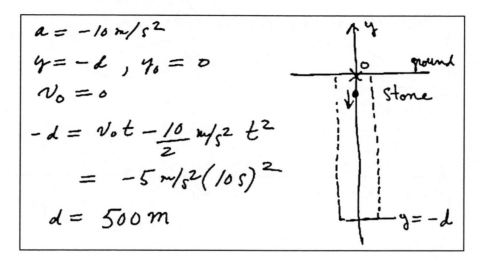

$$a = -10 \text{ m/s}^2$$
$$y = -d \;,\; y_0 = 0$$
$$v_0 = 0$$
$$-d = v_0 t - \frac{10 \text{ m/s}^2}{2} t^2$$
$$= -5 \text{ m/s}^2 (10 \text{ s})^2$$
$$d = 500 \text{ m}$$

- Example 2. a building is 15 stories high (about 150 ft), and a book is dropped from its highest point. How long a time does it take for the book to hit the ground?

$$v_0 = 0 \;,\; y_0 = 150 \text{ ft}$$
$$y - y_0 = v_0 t - \frac{1}{2} 32.2 \text{ ft/s}^2 \, t^2$$
$$-150 \text{ ft} = -16.1 \text{ ft/s}^2 \, t^2$$
$$t = \sqrt{\frac{150}{16.1}} \text{ s} = 3.1 \text{ sec}$$

What is the velocity of the book just before it hits the ground?

$$v - v_0 = -gt. \quad , \quad v_0 = 0$$
$$v = -32.2 \ ft/s^2 (3.1 \ s)$$
$$= -99.8 \ ft/s$$

- Example 3. A ball is thrown upward from the ground (y=0) with an initial velocity of 20 m/s. Take a = −g = −10m/s². How high does the ball travel before falling back to the earth?

$$a = -10 \ m/s^2 \ , \quad v_0 = 20 \ m/s$$

$$y - y_0 = v_0 t - \frac{10 \ m/s^2}{2} t^2$$

$$v - v_0 = -10 \ m/s^2 \ t$$

$$0 - 20 \ m/s = -10 \ m/s^2 \ t$$

$$t = 2 \ sec$$

$$\hookrightarrow d = 20 \ m/s \ (2s) - 5 \ m/s^2 (2s)^2$$

$$= 40m - 20m = 20m$$

A window is 10 m above the ground, and an observer there sees the ball going up and down. At what times does the ball pass the window?

$$y - y_0 = v_0 t - \frac{1}{2} g t^2$$

$$10m = 20 \ m/s \ t - 5 \ m/s^2 \ t^2$$

$$-5t^2 + 20t - 10 = 0$$

top → window ↓

$$y - y_0 = v_0 t - \frac{1}{2} g t^2$$

$$10m - 20m = 0 - 5 \ m/s^2 \ t^2$$

$$-10 = -5t^2 \rightarrow t = \sqrt{2} \ s$$

$$t = 1.4 \ s$$

time to window ↓ = 2 + 1.4 = 3.4 s

Time ground window ↑ = 2 − 1.4 = 0.6 s

Newton's First Law

Objects will either remain at rest or move with a constant velocity if they are free of any influence outside themselves. In the universe, an object alone can move with great speed or small speed, and each condition is really the same to the object. Constant velocity and the state of rest are indistinguishable. Newton observed this fact and it became his first law of motion.

Objects that accelerate must be propelled by forces. The concept of force is associated with acceleration, and is defined operationally in terms of acceleration. If there are no forces, there is no acceleration and conversely.

1. The forces in nature.

One view of the physical world is that it is composed of bits of matter (particles) that interact with one another even though they are separated in space within a vacuum. The following is the current view of the concept of force:

a) Gravitation forces:

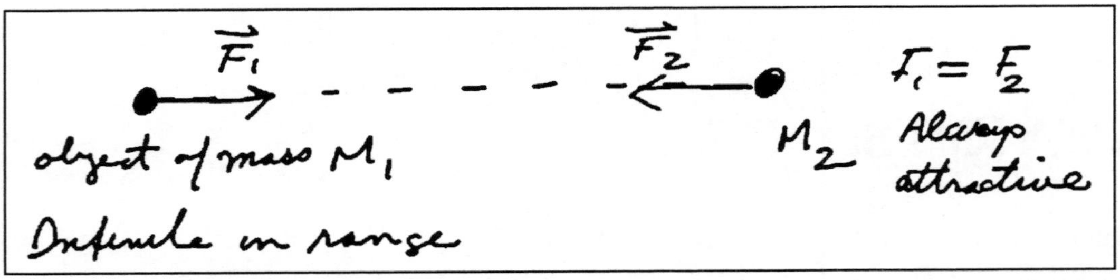

F⃗₁ → - - - - -F⃗₂ ←●
object of mass M₁   M₂   F₁ = F₂
Infinite in range   Always
                                attractive

b) Electromagnetic forces:

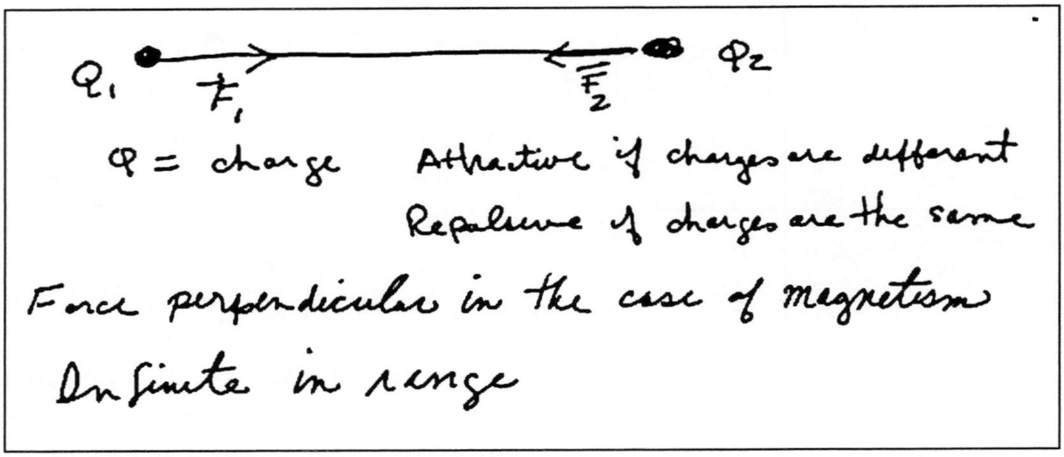

Q₁ ● → ——————— ← ●● Q₂
   F⃗₁   F⃗₂

Q = charge   Attractive if charges are different
             Repulsive if charges are the same
Force perpendicular in the case of magnetism
Infinite in range

c) The strong nuclear force:

Acts in a complicated manner
short ranged (size of the nucleus)
Strongest in nature: 1000 times stronger
than electromagnetic

d) The weak nuclear force - it acts in a complicated manner, is short ranged (about the size of an atomic nucleus) and is responsible for radioactive decay.

e) Levels of understanding:

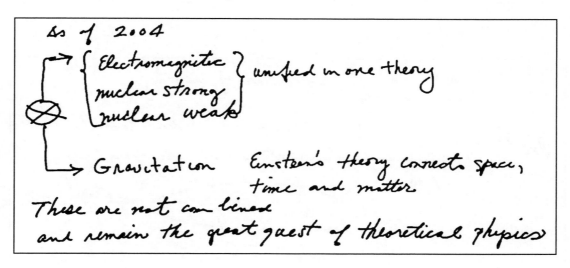

As of 2004

{ Electromagnetic
  nuclear strong
  nuclear weak } unified in one theory

→ Gravitation   Einstein's theory connects space, time and matter

These are not combined
and remain the great quest of theoretical physics

2. Forces as we will use them.

In this course, force will be a push or a pull in a particular direction. This push or pull on an object will cause the object to accelerate by rules given by Newton.

a) Force is a vector quantity.

$$\vec{F_1}$$

8 N

6 N $\vec{F_2}$

Resultant force

$\vec{R}$ F_2

10 N   6 N

8 N $\vec{F_1}$

unit: Newton (N) in International
       Pound (lb) in Engineering

Conversion: 1 lb = 4.448 N

b) Types of forces.

(1) Gravity.

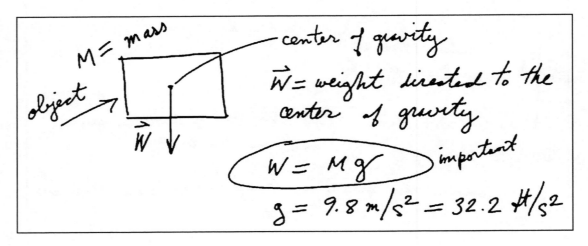

M = mass

object

center of gravity

$\vec{W}$ = weight directed to the center of gravity

$$W = Mg$$ important

$$g = 9.8 \text{ m/s}^2 = 32.2 \text{ ft/s}^2$$

(2) Forces exerted by ropes

$\vec{T}$ $\vec{T}$

T = tension

Must pull on the rope — can't push on a rope

(3)   Contact forces (one object pressed against another).

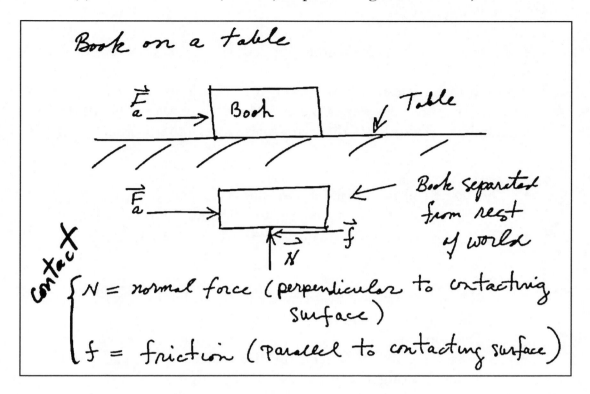

(4)   Applied forces – the force F_a in the above figure.

3.	Newton's first law of motion.

When the vector sums of all the forces that act on a body add to zero, then the body will either remain at rest or in a state of constant velocity. The applications of this law are best visualized by a drawing of the system that is moving. This drawing is called a free-body diagram.

The system can consist of many objects, and these objects are at rest or in a state of constant velocity moving together. We lose no generality by regarding the system to be at rest. To avoid complicating matters by allowing the objects to be extended and therefore capable of rotating, we will only consider point objects. This subject is actually important for engineers to master, especially Civil Engineers, who need to determine the stresses in building materials.

a) The idea of a free-body diagram applied to the first law

A design technique that works even for complex systems is based on a free-body force diagram. One first draws the system as clearly and accurately as possible. If there are many interacting elements, one of them is isolated:

- The single object is place in two-dimension space by drawing in x and y axes, and the units of measure are indicate on the axes.
- The forces that act on this object are then carefully identified and drawn. These forces are:

  1. Gravity. It act downward and has the value m g, were m is the mass of the object and g = 9.8 m/s^2.
  2. Tension. If a rope is attached to the object under consideration, its affect on the object is to exert a force directed along the rope. Note that ropes can only pull, not push.
  3. Contact forces. These forces exist if the object under consideration is touching another object through there surfaces. There are two contact forces, one is perpendicular to the surface and one is parallel to the surface. The perpendicular force is called the normal force, and the parallel force is called friction. If the contacting surfaces are smooth, there is no friction.
  4. If an agent external to the system pushes or pulls on the object, its effect must be added to the mix. This is called an applied force.

- Since the object is at rest, all these forces must balance. As force is a vector quantity, it is easiest to draw each force as an x and y component if they are not already so oriented. The first law then requires that

$$\text{The sum of all the x forces} = 0,$$
$$\text{The sum of all the y forces} = 0.$$

The solution of these equations allows us to evaluate unknown quantities. Remember the whole point of this process is to determine the values of all the forces that act on the object as most will not be known beforehand.

- If the system is complex, isolating one object may not give us all the force values. In that event, another object in the system needs to be analyzed in exactly the same way, and the process continues until all the forces are determined.

b) Example 1.

A book at rest on a table showing all the forces that act on the book.

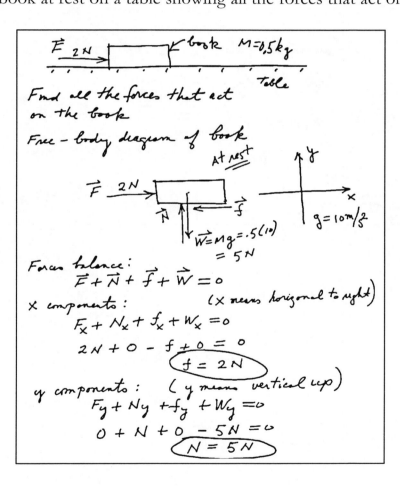

c) Example 2.

Two horizontal forces act on a wagon, 550 N forward and 300 N backward. What third force is needed to produce a net force of zero?

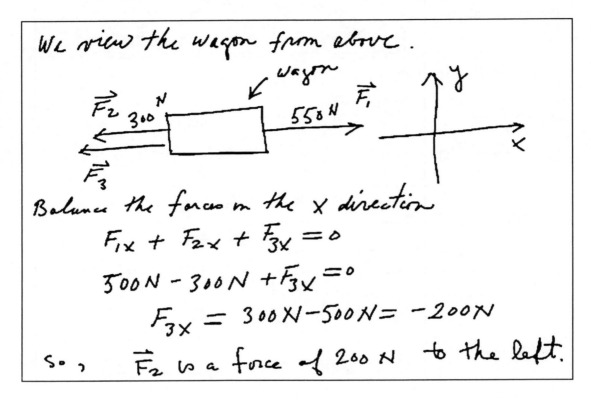

We view the wagon from above.

Balance the forces in the x direction

$$F_{1x} + F_{2x} + F_{3x} = 0$$

$$500N - 300N + F_{3x} = 0$$

$$F_{3x} = 300N - 500N = -200N$$

So, $\vec{F_2}$ is a force of 200 N to the left.

d) Example 3.

A box of mass 100 kg is suspended at rest above the ground by a pulley system as shown below. What is the tension in the rope that runs over the pulleys?

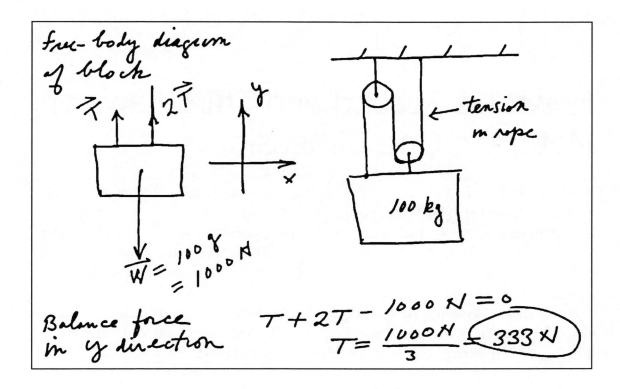

free-body diagram
of block

$\vec{T}$ $2\vec{T}$ y

$\overline{W} = 100\,g$
$= 1000\,N$

tension
in rope

$100\,kg$

Balance force
in y direction

$T + 2T - 1000\,N = 0$

$T = \dfrac{1000\,N}{3} = \boxed{333\,N}$

CHAPTER 4

Newton's Second and Third Laws of Motion in One Dimension

Newton followed Galileo in associating a force with acceleration. But Newton quantified and universalized the connection. It is a connection between space, time and mass with space and time still absolute and independent of each other. In the early part of the twentieth century, Albert Einstein would associate space, time and mass as dependent characteristics of reality.

Newton asserted that a body of mass M when acted upon by forces that add as vectors to a resultant force F will accelerate in the direction of F. The result is that the body will accelerate according to

$$F = M a, \ a = \text{acceleration}.$$

1.   Applications of the second law.

The following examples will be solved in a similar manner to what we did in the last chapter. Free body diagrams are drawn of the system in question, and the forces are drawn on the system objects. Now, however, the forces do not balance, so acceleration must be added to the drawing in the direction of the unbalanced force.

a) Example.

Let's reconsider the last example worked out in the last chapter but changed so that the forces do not balance. A box of mass 100 kg is suspended above the ground by a pulley system as shown below, and the tension in the rope that runs over the pulleys is found to be 200 N. What is the acceleration of the block (magnitude and direction)?

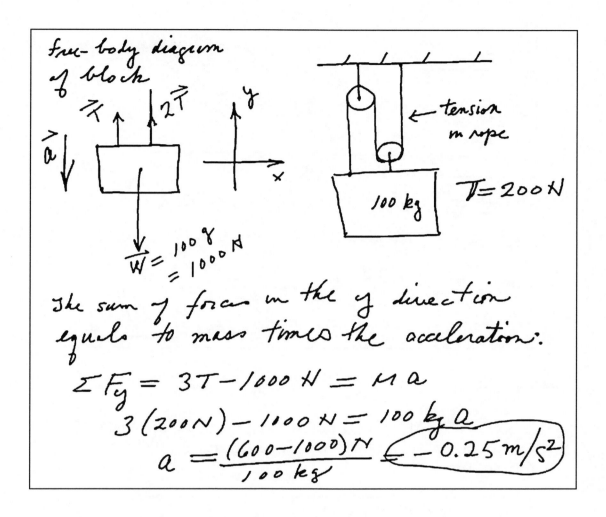

free-body diagram
of block

$\vec{T}$ $2\vec{T}$ y

$\vec{a}$

$\vec{W} = 100\,g$
$= 1000\,N$

← tension
in rope

100 kg $T = 200\,N$

The sum of forces in the y direction
equals to mass times the acceleration:

$$\Sigma F_y = 3T - 1000\,N = Ma$$
$$3(200\,N) - 1000\,N = 100\,kg\,a$$
$$a = \frac{(600 - 1000)\,N}{100\,kg} \qquad -0.25\,m/s^2$$

b) Example 1:

An object of mass m_1 experiences an acceleration of 'a' when acted upon by a force F in the x direction. If a force of 4F act on another mass m_2, this mass accelerates at the rate of 10 a. If m_1 = 4 kg, what is the value of m_2?

$$\vec{F} \quad m_1$$

$$\Sigma F_x = F = m_1 a \quad (1)$$

$$4\vec{F} \quad m_2$$

$$a' = 10\, a$$

$$\Sigma F_x = 4F = m_2 a' = 10 m_2 a \quad (2)$$

Combine equations (1) and (2):

$$F = m_1 a = \frac{10\, m_2\, a}{4}$$

$$\rightarrow m_2 = \frac{4}{10} m_1 = 0.4(4\,kg) = \boxed{1.6\,kg}$$

c) Example 2:

A box of mass M = 2 kg is pulled along a rough horizontal surface by a rope and pulley system. The box accelerates at 2 m/s². What is the force of friction?

$$M = 2\,kg \quad a = 2\,m/s^2 \quad T = 10\,N$$

rough

free-body diagram of box

$$M \qquad T = 10\,N \qquad y$$

$$f$$

$$N \quad W = 2(10) = 20\,N$$

$$\Sigma F_x = T - f = M a$$

$$10\,N - f = 2\,kg(2\,m/s^2) = 4N$$

$$f = 10\,N - 4\,N = \boxed{6\,N}$$

d) Example 3:

A box of mass M = 2 kg is lowered on a rope accelerating downward with an acceleration of a. The tension in the rope is 5 N.

(1) What is the acceleration?
(2) What is the tension in the rope if the box accelerates upward with the acceleration a?

$$(1)$$
$$\Sigma F_y = T - W = Ma$$

$$5N - 2kg\,(10 m/s^2) = 2kg\,a$$

$$a = \frac{5N - 20N}{2\,kg} = -7.5 m/s^2$$

$T = 5N$

$$(2)$$
$$\Sigma F_y = T' - W = Ma'$$

$$T' - 20N = 2kg\,(7.5 m/s^2)$$

$$T' = 20N + 15N = 35N$$

$$a' = 7.5 m/s^2$$

e) Example 4.

Two masses M_1 = 6 kg and M_2 = 10 kg are tied together my a rope that rounds around pulleys as shown. The mass M_1 accelerates downward with an acceleration a, and the mass M_2 moves upward with an acceleration a/2. We want to find the acceleration and the tension in the rope.

Mass m_1

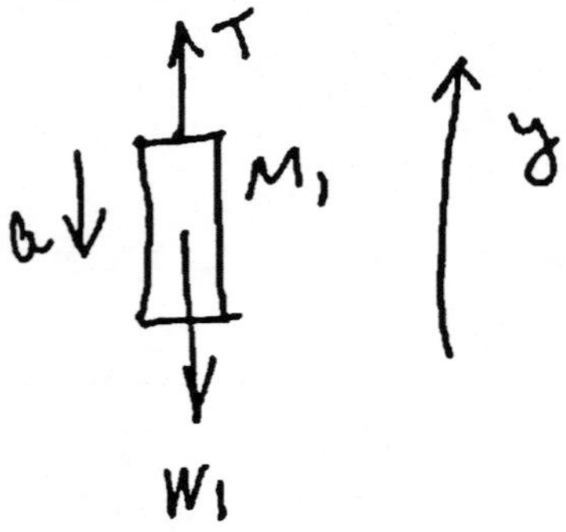

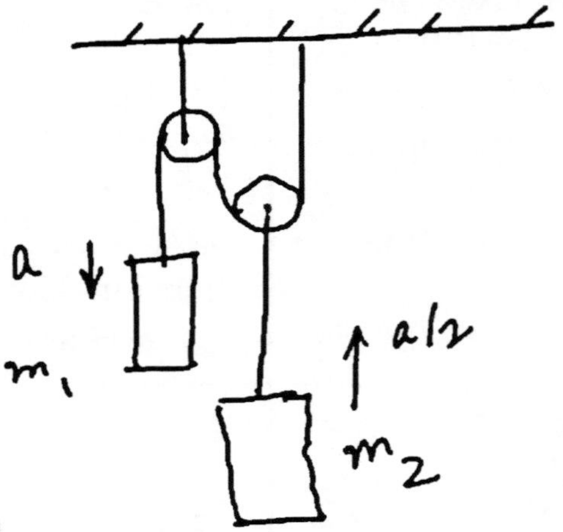

$$\Sigma F_y = T - W_1 = M_1 (-a)$$
$$T - 60N = -6 kg \, a$$

Mass M_2

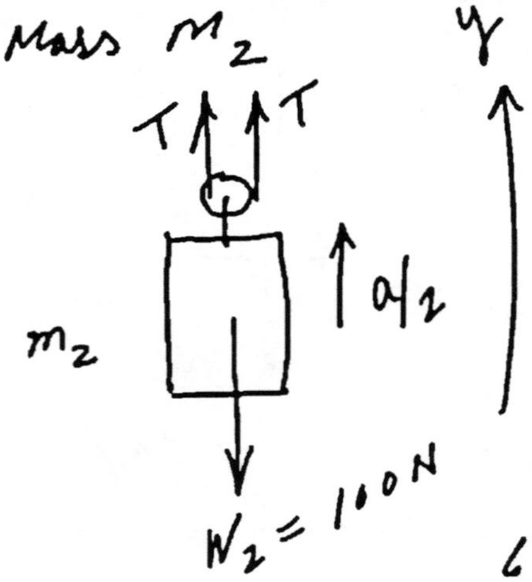

$$\Sigma F_y = 2T - 100N = 10 kg \, \frac{a}{2}$$

$$2T - 100N = 5 kg \, a$$

$$T = -6a + 60 = \frac{100 + 5a}{2}$$

$$60 - 50 = 2.5a + 6a$$

$$a = \frac{10}{8.5} = \boxed{1.18 \, m/s^2}$$

The tension is
$$T = 50 + 2.5 (1.18) = \boxed{53N}$$

f) Example 5.

Two blocks of mass $M_1 = 2$ kg and $M_2 = 3$ kg are tied by a rope and pulled by a force of 10 N along a smooth horizontal surface as shown below. What is the acceleration of the blocks?

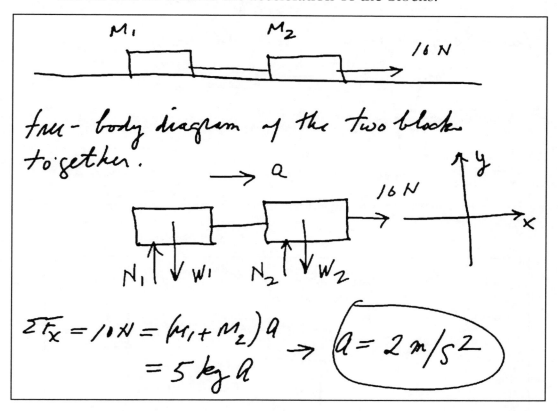

$$\Sigma \vec{F}_x = 10N = (M_1 + M_2)a$$
$$= 5 kg\, a \quad \rightarrow \quad \boxed{a = 2\, m/s^2}$$

2.   Introduction of the third law and examples.

The third law is: if a body A exerts a force F on a body B, then body B exerts a force -F on body A.

a) Example 1.

Two blocks tied together by a rope. A mass $M_1 = 2$ kg and $M_2 = 3$ kg are tied by a rope and pulled by a force of 10 N along a smooth horizontal surface as shown below. What is the acceleration of the blocks? What is the tension in the rope stretched between the blocks?

Solution

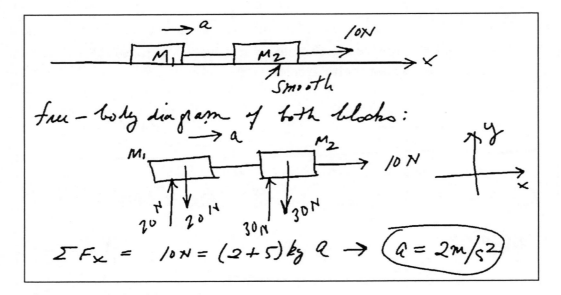

$$\Sigma F_x = 10N = (2+5)kg \; a \rightarrow \boxed{a = 2m/s^2}$$

free - body diagram of M_1 :

$$\Sigma F_x = T = M_1 a = 2kg \left(2m/s^2\right)$$
$$\boxed{= 4 N}$$

For the same problem, verify that the force that mass 1 exerts on mass 2 satisfies Newton's third law.

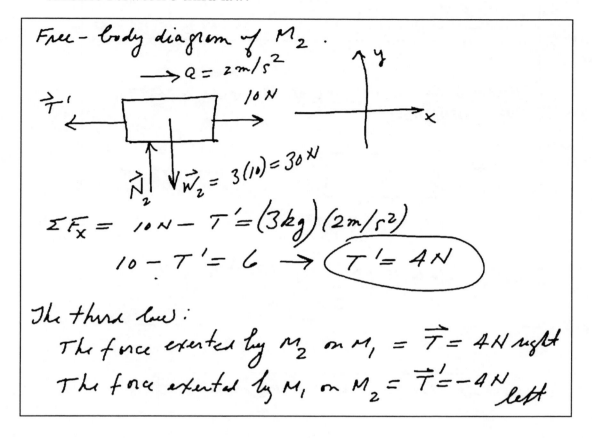

Free - body diagram of M_2.

$\longrightarrow a = 2 m/s^2$

$\vec{T}'$

$10 N$

$\vec{N}_2$ $\quad \vec{W}_2 = 3(10) = 30 N$

$\Sigma F_x = 10 N - T' = (3 kg)(2 m/s^2)$

$10 - T' = 6 \rightarrow \boxed{T' = 4N}$

The third law:

The force exerted by M_2 on M_1 = $\vec{T}$ = $4N$ right

The force exerted by M_1 on M_2 = $\vec{T}' = -4N$ left

b) Example 2.

Two blocks pushed against each other on a smooth level surface. We will pattern this problem on the one above. The mass on the left M1 = 2 kg, and the mass on the right is M2 = 3 kg. The mass on the left is pushed by an applied force of 10 N as shown below. Find the acceleration of the system and the force that each block exerts on the other.

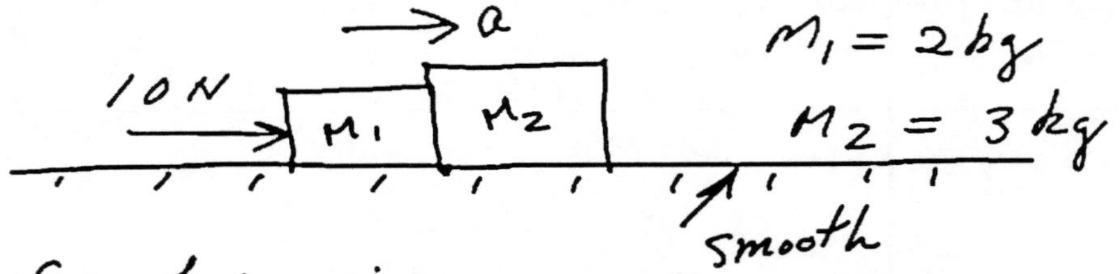

$\longrightarrow a$

$10 N$

M_1 | M_2

$M_1 = 2 kg$

$M_2 = 3 kg$

smooth

free-body diagram of the two masses together:

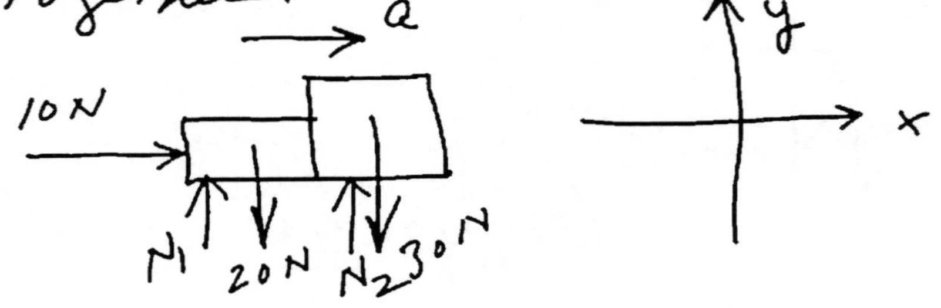

$\longrightarrow a$

$10 N$

N_1 $20 N$ N_2 $30 N$

$\uparrow y$ $\longrightarrow x$

$\Sigma F_x = 10 N = (m_1 + m_2) a = 5 kg \, a$

$\longrightarrow \boxed{a = 2 m/s^2}$

We next find the force that M_2 exerts on M_1.

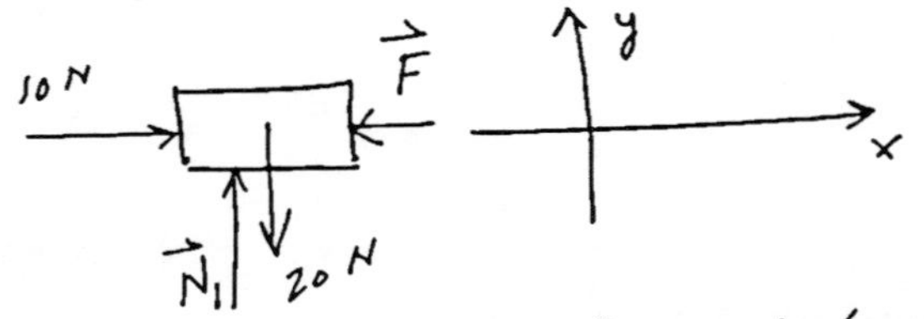

$10 N$ $\overrightarrow{F}$

$\overrightarrow{N_1}$ $20 N$

$\uparrow y$ $\longrightarrow x$

$\Sigma F_x = 10 N - F = M_1 \, a = 2 kg (2 m/s^2)$

$F = 10 N - 4 N = \boxed{6 N}$

Verify: the force on M_2 is $-\overrightarrow{F}$

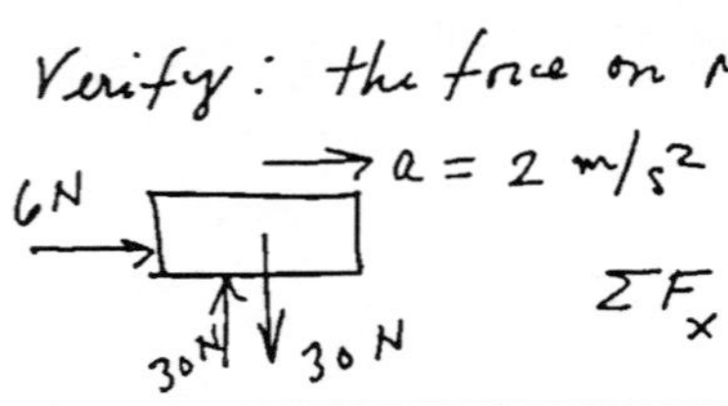

$6 N$ $\longrightarrow a = 2 m/s^2$

$30 N$ $30 N$

$\Sigma F_x = 6 N = (3 kg)(2 m/s^2) = 6$ ✓

c) Two books on an elevator.

Find the forces that each book exerts on the other using Newton's third law.

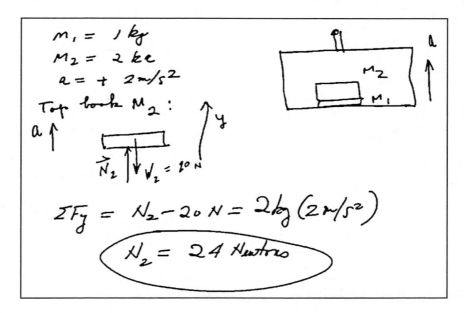

d) A problem involving friction and constant accelerated motion.

A box of 500 kg slides along a rough horizontal surface with an initial velocity of vo = 30 m/s. It comes to rest in 10 seconds. What is the acceleration of the box and how far does it move before coming to rest?

What is the force of friction that acts on the box?

free - body diagram of box
$a = -3 m/s^2$
v
f
N $5000 N$

$\Sigma F_x = -f = 500 kg (-3 m/s^2) \rightarrow \boxed{f = 1500 N}$

---

3.   Momentum and the Second Law.

It turns out that the second law has to be modified. Einstein's special theory of relativity will be discussed in the next course, but before we leave the second law, let's reform it to illustrate this vital new physical parameter.

The momentum of a particle of mass M moving with a velocity v is defined by

$$P = M v.$$

Momentum is a vector quantity, and it contains all three fundamental parameters – space, time and mass. The unit is kg m/s. Newton's second law is

$$F = M a = M (\Delta v / \Delta t) = (M \Delta v) / \Delta t.$$

Here the "Δ" signifies a difference in the quantity v or t. However, if M is constant, then a change in the momentum of a particle is

$$\Delta P = \Delta(M v) = M \Delta v.$$

With this result, we see that the net force acting on a mass M is

$$F = (M \, \Delta v) / \Delta t = \Delta P / \Delta t.$$

In words, this says that the net force acting on a mass is equal to the rate of change of the momentum. So, the momentum of a moving object with mass M will change only when an unbalance force act on it.

This may seem to be another example of scientists inventing new names just for the sake of the exercise. However, the form of Newton's second law in terms of momentum is actually the one that survives Einstein's theory of special relativity. It does so because in relativity the mass of a moving object changes with speed– it is not constant. So, here we see an example of Newton's worldview needing modification.

CHAPTER 5

Motion in Two Dimensions and Gravitation

The three independent directions of motion are each driven to acceleration components by resultant forces in each direction, and the three component accelerations tells us how the object moves in time. This chapter will discuss circular motion and gravity. Newton's law of universal gravitation will be presented and combined with circular motion to describe satellite motion.

1. Circular motion is accelerated motion.

Consider a mass M moving with a constant speed v in a circle of radius R. The mass is held in the circle by a rope whose tension is T. Consider the mass to be moving in a smooth horizontal plane, so that the free-body diagram for the mass is shown below:

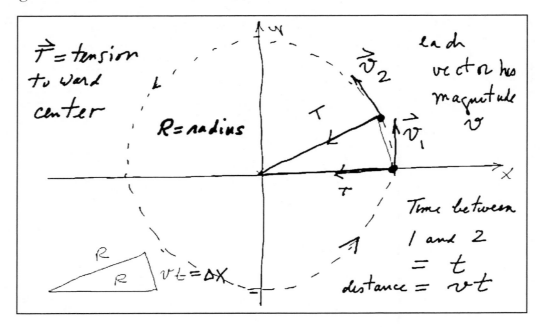

As the mass moves around the circle between the points 1 and 2 shown, the vector velocity keeps turning inward. We shown this in the next picture:

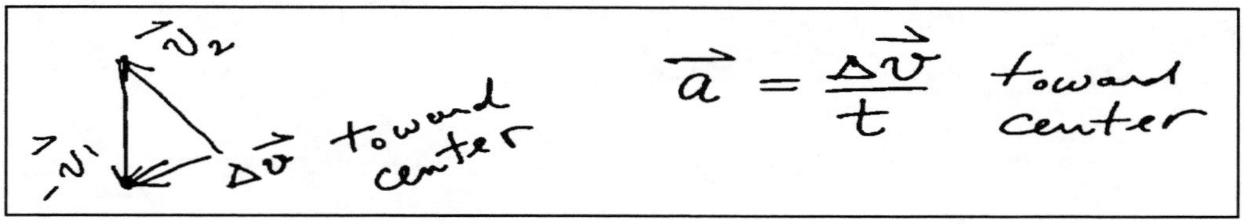

That is, a mass moving in a circle of radius R with a constant speed v accelerates toward the center of the circle with an acceleration

$$a = v^2/R, \text{ toward the center of the circle,}$$

and since the only force toward the center is the tension T, Newton's second law gives

$$T = M a = M v^2/R.$$

a) Example.

A ball of mass 5 kg is spun in a horizontal circle of radius 0.5 m on a string. It moves with a constant speed and makes one revolution in 2 seconds. What is the speed of the ball and its acceleration?

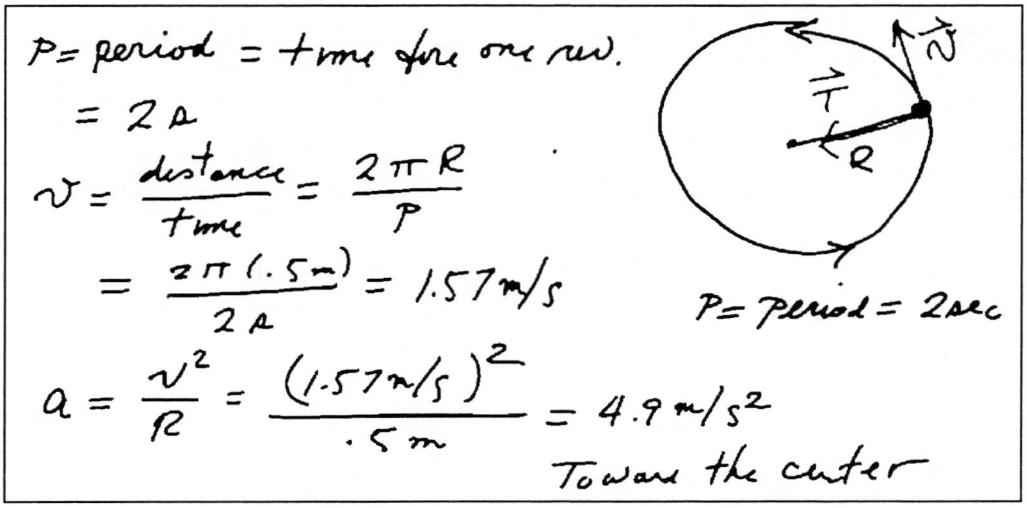

What is the tension in the rope?

$$\Sigma F_{center} = T = M a_{center}$$

$$T = (5 kg)(4.9 m/s^2)$$

$$= 24.7 N \text{ toward the center}$$

free body dia.

The string which keeps the ball moving in a circle will break when its tension exceeds 30N. What is the period of the motion when this limit is reached?

$$T = 30 N = m v^2/R = \frac{5 kg \; v^2}{.5 m} = 10 v^2 \frac{kg}{m}$$

$$10 v^2 = 30 \rightarrow v = \sqrt{3} \, m/s = 1.7 \, m/s$$

$$v = \frac{2\pi R}{P}$$

$$P = \frac{2\pi R}{v} = \frac{2\pi (.5m)}{1.73 \, m/s} = 1.8 \, sec$$

b) Effect of the rotation of the Earth on an object on its surface.

The radius of the Earth is R = 6400 km, and its spin period is 24 hours. Find the acceleration of an apple of mass m at the equator and compare it to the acceleration due to gravity.

$$P = \text{Period} = 24 \text{ hours} \left(\frac{3600 \, s}{h} \right)$$

$$= 86,400 \, sec$$

$$v = \text{speed of apple}$$

$$= \frac{2 \pi R_e}{P} = \frac{2 \pi \, 6.4 \times 10^6 \, m}{86,400 \, sec}$$

$$= 465 \, m/s$$

$$a_{center} = v^2/R_e = \frac{(465 \, m/s)^2}{6.4 \times 10^6 \, m} = \boxed{0.034 \, m/s^2}$$

The acceleration due to gravity $= 9.8 \, m/s^2$

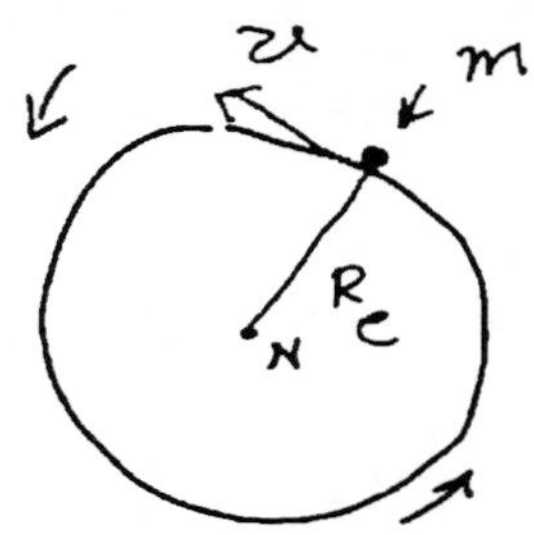

We see that the effect of the spin of the earth is 0.3% of gravity.

---

2. The motion of a projectile.

The motion of a mass M moving horizontally above the surface of the earth is motion that must be described in two. The only force acting on the mass is gravity, hence the mass accelerates vertically downward with an acceleration $-g = -10 \text{ m/s}^2$.

The horizontal motion has no acceleration as there are no horizontal forces (neglecting air friction). The subsequent motion is a parabola depicted below:

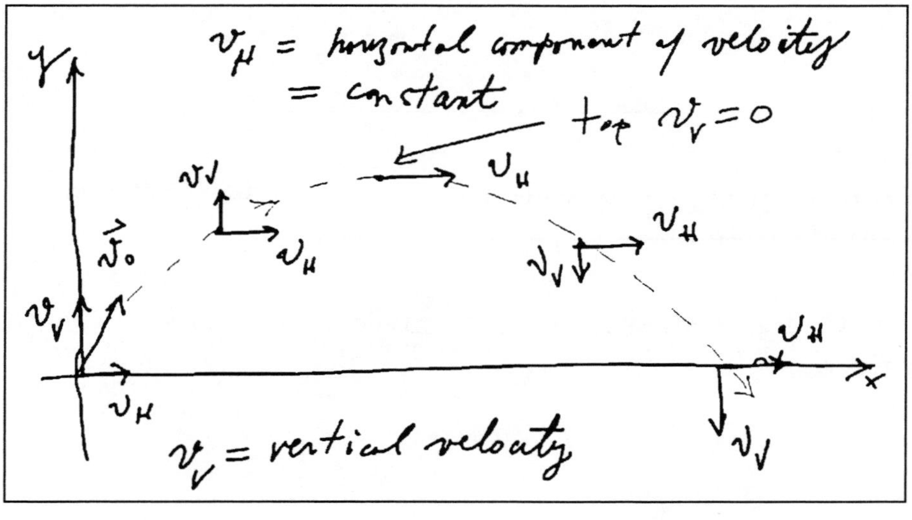

| 3. | Newton's law of motion for a projectile and the equations of motion. |

We first draw a free-body diagram for a projectile moving above the surface of the earth:

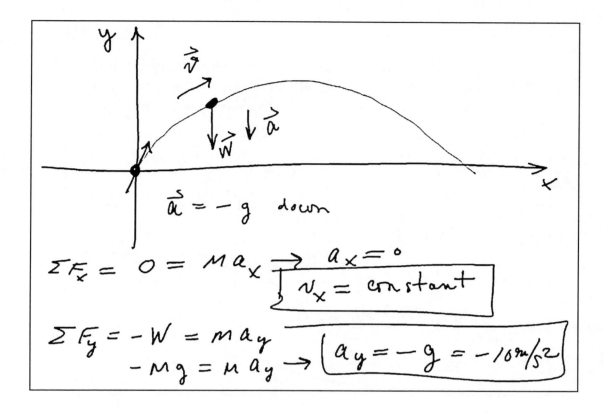

$$\Sigma F_x = 0 = M a_x \longrightarrow a_x = 0$$

$$\boxed{\nu_x = constant}$$

$$\Sigma F_y = -W = M a_y$$
$$-Mg = M a_y \longrightarrow \boxed{a_y = -g = -10 \, m/s^2}$$

The equations of motion in the x and y directions are:

x direction horizontal
$$\nu_x = constant \quad \boxed{x - x_0 = \nu_x t}$$

y direction vertical
$$a_y = -g$$
$$\boxed{\begin{aligned} \nu_y - \nu_{0y} &= -g t \\ y - y_0 &= \nu_{0y} t - \frac{1}{2} g t^2 \end{aligned}}$$

a) Example.

A bowling ball of mass M rolls off the edge of a cliff horizontally with a horizontal velocity of 45 ft/s. It falls to the ground in 4 seconds. What is the height of the cliff above the ground level?

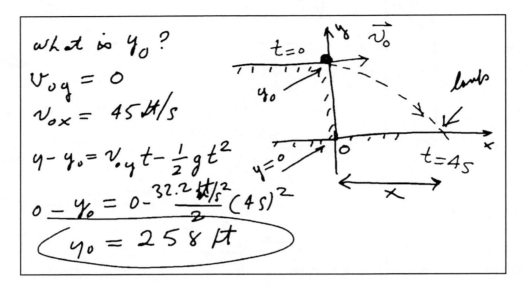

What are the horizontal and vertical components of the velocity of the bowling ball just before it hits the ground?

How far from the base of the cliff does the bowling ball travel?

$$x - x_0 = v_x t = 45 \, ft/s \, (4s)$$
$$= 180 \, ft$$

velocity just before the ball hits the ground.

$$v_x = 45 \, ft/s$$
$$v_y - v_{0y} = -g \cdot t$$
$$v_y - 0 = -10 \, (4s)$$
$$v_y = -40 \, ft/s$$

45 ft/s

40 ft/s

b) Projectile motion.

A baseball hits a wall 100 meters away. It's initial velocity has an x-component of 20 m/s and a y-component of 30 m/s. How long does it take for the ball to reach the wall?

wall

$v_{0y} = 30 \, m/s$

$o \quad v_{0x} = 20 \, m/s$

$x = 100 \, m$

$$x - x_0 = v_x t \Rightarrow t = \frac{100 \, m}{20 \, m/s} = \boxed{5 \, sec}$$

How high up the wall does the ball hit?

The time to hit the wall is 5 sec.

$$y - y_0 = v_{oy} t - \frac{1}{2} g t^2 \quad , \quad y_0 = 0$$

$$v_{oy} = 30 \, m/s$$

$$y = 30 \, m/s \left(5 \, sec\right) - \frac{10 \, m/s^2}{2} \left(5 \, sec\right)^2$$

$$= 150 \, m - 125 \, m = \boxed{25 \, m}$$

Is the baseball moving upward or downward just before it hits the wall?

$$v_x = \text{always the same} = 20 \, m/s$$

$$v_y - v_{oy} = -g t$$

$$v_y = v_{oy} - g t = 30 \, m/s - \left(10 \, m/s^2\right)\left(5 \, sec\right)$$

$$\boxed{= -20 \, m/s \qquad downward}$$

4.   Newton's Law of Gravitation

We have been working with the force of gravity as it exists at or just above the surface of the Earth. Because of the relative size of the Earth and us, this gravitational effect seems to be constant and directed downward. However, if one moves away from the Earth's surface, one finds that gravity decreases, and its effect for the spherical Earth is symmetrical. Newton had a great success in applying his laws of motion to the motion of the planets after he presented one additional idea and one additional assumption.

The assumption is that massive objects exert forces on each other, consistent with the three laws, but they can do this even though great distances apart. This "action at a distance" notion was philosophically challenge by many of his time, like Leibniz. In fact, the modern point of view is that objects interact even though separated by through "force fields" that permeate space. Moreover, the gravitational effect is due to the distortion of space and time by matter[7]. But let's stay on the historical line with our story with the promise that we will return to this mysterious thing called gravity.

a) Newton's universal law of gravitation.

The gravitational force between two masses is attractive, proportional to the product of their masses and inversely proportional to the square of the distance between them.

If one on the masses is the Earth, with mass M_{earth}, and the other is an object of mass m on the surface a distance of R_{earth} from the center of the Earth, the law becomes

$$W = m\,g = G\,M_{earth}\,m\,/\,R_{earth}^{2},$$

so the "g factor" is

$$g = 9.8 \text{ m/s2} = G\,M_{earth}\,/\,R_{earth}^{2}.$$

---

[7] Einstein's general theory of relativity describes space and time as curved by the presence of matter: Annalen der Physik, vol. 49, 1916.

This suggests that in dealing with the law of gravitation, the earth can be used as a standard. This will avoid looking up a lot of planetary constants. We need only remember the value of g and ratios.

b) The law of gravitation on any planet.

We will use the Earth as a standard. The weight W of a mass m near a planet is

$$W = mg \, M_{planet}/R^2 \text{ (constant)},$$

where

$$g = 9.8 \text{ m/s}^2,$$
$$M_{planet} = \text{mass of the planet},$$
$$R = \text{distance of the mass m from the center of the planet.}$$

This equation must work on the surface of the earth, so the constant can be evaluated:

$$W = mg = mg \, M_{earth} / R_{earth}^2 \text{ (constant)},$$

so

$$\text{constant} = R_{earth}^2 / M_{earth.}$$

The bottom line (equation to remember) is

$$W = W_{earth} \, M_{planet}/R^2 \, R_{earth}^2 / M_{earth}$$
$$W = m \, g \, (M_{planet}/M_{earth}) \, (R_{earth}/R)^2.$$

For emphases:

W = weight on a planet or above the earth

$$= mg \left(\frac{M_{planet}}{M_{earth}} \right) \left(\frac{R_{earth}}{R_{planet}} \right)^2$$

where

mg = weight on the surface of the earth

$g = 10 \ m/s^2$

For an earth satellite at a distance R from the center of the earth

$$W = \text{weight of satellite} = mg \left(\frac{R_{earth}}{R} \right)^2.$$

For reference

$$M_{earth} = 6.0 \times 10^{24} \ kg$$

$$R_{earth} = 6.4 \times 10^{6} \ m \ (4000 \ miles)$$

c) Example 1.

What is the weight of an object at rest on the surface of the moon, where $M_{moon} / M_{earth} = 0.0124$ and $R_{moon}/R_{earth} = 0.276$. The earth weight of the object is 120 lbs.

$$W = (mg) \left(\frac{M_{moon}}{M_{earth}} \right) \left(\frac{R_{earth}}{R_{moon}} \right)^2$$

$$= 120 \ lbs \ (0.0124) \left(\frac{1}{.276} \right)^2$$

$$= 120 \ lbs \ 0.163$$

$$= 19.5 \ lbs$$

d) Example 2.

An earth satellite of mass 1000 kg is a height of 1.6×10^6 m above the surface of the Earth. If the radius of the Earth is 6.4×10^6 m, what is the weight of the satellite, its acceleration and the speed of the satellite in its orbit?

$$W = mg \left(\frac{R_{earth}}{R} \right)^2 \quad \text{no mass factn}$$

$$= 10,000 \, N \left(\frac{6.4}{8.0} \right)^2$$

$$= 6410 \, N$$

$$W = 6400 \, N = M v^2 / R$$

$$a = v^2 / R = \frac{6400 \, N}{1000 \, kg} = 6.4 \, m/s^2$$

$$v = \left[\frac{6400 \left(8 \times 10^6 \right)}{1000} \right]^{1/2} = 7.2 \times 10^3 \, m/s$$

$R_e = 4000 \, mile$

$R = 5000 \, miles$

---

5.   Communication satellites (geosynchronous).

A geosynchronous satellite stays directly above a point on the equator and serves as an easy target to bounce radio waves from one point on the surface of the earth to another. They number in the thousands and have electronically linked all areas on the surface of the Earth. As the satellite hovers over a spot on the equator, it must rotate with the same speed as the earth, and hence its period of circular motion is 24 hours.

a) The radius of the orbit.

The weight of a satellite with mass m is

$$W = mg \left(\frac{R_e}{R}\right)^2$$

$$g = 10 \, m/s^2$$

Newton's second law:

$$\Sigma F_{center} = -W = m \, v^2/R$$

$$\rightarrow \, \cancel{m} g \left(R_e^2/R^2\right) = \cancel{m} \, v^2/\cancel{R}$$

$$v^2 = g \, R_e^2/R = 10 \, m/s^2 \frac{\left(6.4 \times 10^6 \, m\right)^2}{R}$$

$$\boxed{v^2 = 4.1 \times 10^{14}/R}$$

The period of the motion is

$$P = 24 \, hours = \frac{2\pi R}{v}$$

$$v = \frac{2\pi R}{24 \, hrs} \left(\frac{hr}{3600 \, s}\right) = \frac{2\pi}{24(3600)} R$$

$$\boxed{= 7.27 \times 10^{-5} R}$$

So, the radius of the orbit is

$$v^2 = \frac{4.1 \times 10^{14}}{R} = 5.29 \times 10^{-9} R^2$$

$$\rightarrow R^3 = \frac{4.1 \times 10^{14}}{5.29 \times 10^{-9}} = 7.75 \times 10^{22} \, m^3$$

$$R = \left(7.75 \times 10^{22}\right)^{1/3} = \boxed{4.26 \times 10^7 \, m}$$

Therefore, the radius of the orbit of the geo-satellite is R = 4.26×10^7 m. The radius of the Earth is R$_{earth}$ = 6.4×10^6 m. The orbit is (4.26×10^7 m/6.4×10^6 m) = 6.6 times the radius of the Earth, or the orbit of a communication satellite is

$$R_{geo} = 6.6 \times 4000 \text{miles} = 26,000 \text{ miles},$$

and the height of the satellite above the surface of the earth is

$$Height_{geo} = 26,000 - 4000 = 22,000 \text{ miles}.$$

b) The "g factor" at the height of the orbit.

c) The tilt of a satellite dish.

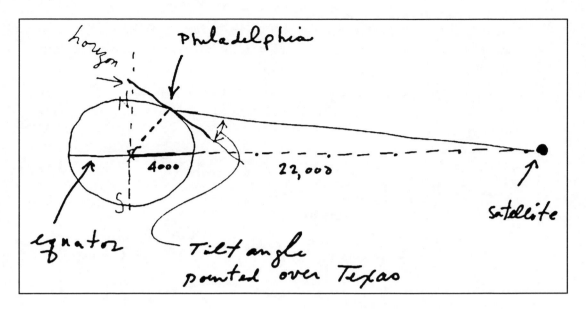

d) Example.

Consider A 600 kg geosynchronous satellite has an orbital radius of 6.6 the radius of the Earth. What is the weight of the satellite and its acceleration at this height?

$$W = mg\left(\frac{R_e}{R}\right)^2 = mg\left(\frac{R_e}{6.6\,R_e}\right)^2$$

$$= (600\,kg)(10\,m/s^2)\left(\frac{1}{43.6}\right)$$

$$\boxed{= 138\,N}$$

$$W = Ma \quad (\text{Newton's second law})$$

$$a = \frac{-138\,N}{600\,kg} = -0.229\,m/s^2 \; \text{downward}$$

e) Example.

A golf ball travels a distance of 300 yards = 900 (.3048m/ft) = 274 m over the surface of the earth. This will happen if both the initial vertical and horizontal velocities are 37 m/s.

What is the g-factor on the moon given that moon has a mass 0.0123 times the mass of the earth, and a radius 0.273 times that of the earth?

$$W_{moon} = mg \left(\frac{M_{moon}}{M_{earth}}\right)\left(\frac{R_{earth}}{R_{moon}}\right)^2$$

$$= mg \, (0.0123)\left(\frac{1}{.273}\right)^2 = .165 \, mg$$

$$= m \, g_{moon}$$

$$g_{moon} = .165 \, g = \boxed{1.65 \, m/s^2}$$

What is the time of flight of the ball on the earth and the moon?

At the top, $v_y = 0$

$$v_y - v_{o_y} = -gt$$

$$0 - 37 \, m/s = -gt$$

$$t = \frac{37 \, m/s}{10 \, m/s^2} = \underline{3.7 \, sec \, (earth)}$$

$$t = \frac{37 \, m/s}{g_{moon}} = \frac{37 \, m/s}{1.65 \, m/s^2} = 22.4 \, sec$$

$$time \; of \; flight = 2t = \begin{cases} 7.4 \, sec \quad earth \\ 44.8 \, sec \quad moon \end{cases}$$

How far does the golf ball travel on the moon?

distance traveled on earth
$$= X - X_0 = v_x t = 37 \, m/s \, (7.4 \, sec) = 273 \, m$$
$$X - X_0 = v_x \, t_{moon} \qquad\qquad = 300 \, yds$$
$$= 37 \, m/s \, (44.8 \, sec)$$
$$= 1658 \, m \neq 1822 \, yards$$

Work and Energy

The concept of energy in physics and technology is central and essential in understanding physical processes. Energy in its various forms and its transformations from one form to another provide the picture by which reality is viewed today as well as it was in the classical Newtonian era.

We will start with energy in its elemental form —work done by forces - then the energy of motion and position. These are called the mechanical forms of energy. We will then discuss the transformation of mechanical energy into heat energy.

1. The idea of mechanical energy and work from an example

a) A simple problem using Newton's laws of motion.

A block of mass 5 kg moves on a rough table top pulled by a rope horizontally. It starts from rest and moves a distance of 5 m by the action of the rope whose tension is 5 N and a friction force of 2 N that opposes the motion. Find the velocity of the block at the point that it has moved 5 m?

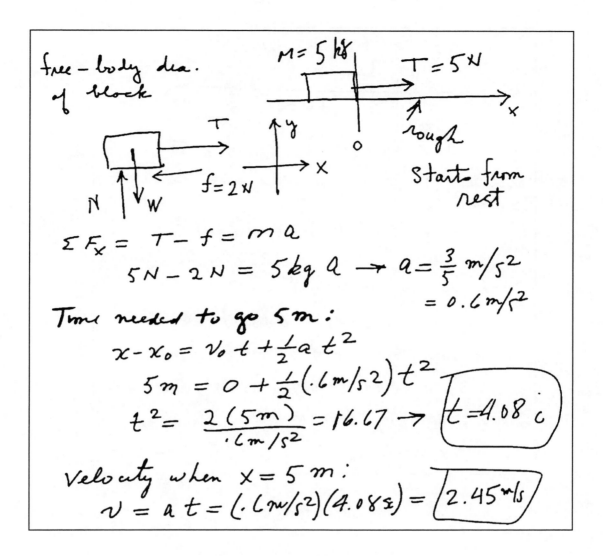

free-body dia. of block

$M = 5 \text{ kg}$

$T = 5 N$

rough

starts from rest

$$\Sigma F_x = T - f = m a$$
$$5N - 2N = 5 kg\, a \rightarrow a = \frac{3}{5} \, m/s^2$$
$$= 0.6 \, m/s^2$$

Time needed to go 5m:
$$x - x_0 = v_0 t + \frac{1}{2} a t^2$$
$$5m = 0 + \frac{1}{2}(.6 \, m/s^2) t^2$$
$$t^2 = \frac{2(5m)}{.6 \, m/s^2} = 16.67 \rightarrow \boxed{t = 4.08 \, s}$$

Velocity when $x = 5 \, m$:
$$v = a t = (.6 \, m/s^2)(4.08 s) = \boxed{2.45 \, m/s}$$

b) The concept work done by a force.

Definition. The work done by a force F as an object moves between two points on the x-axis is F_x $(x_2 - x_1)$, where F_x is the component of the force F in the x-direction. Consider a box moving along x under the influence of several forces:

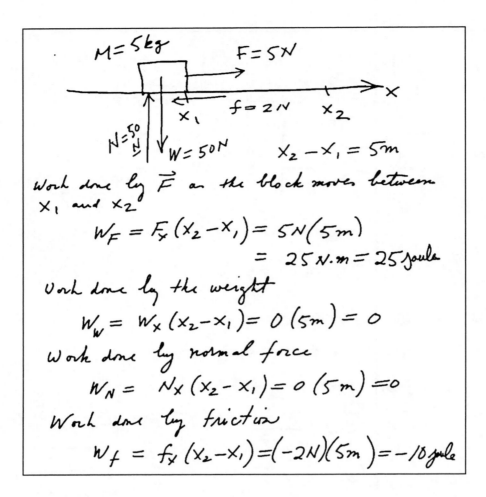

c) The total work done by all the forces.

$$W_{total} = W_F + W_W + W_N + W_f$$
$$= 25 \text{ joules} + 0 + 0 - 10 \text{ joules} = 15 \text{ joules}$$

The unit of work and energy is the joule.

2. Work and kinetic energy.

There is energy in motion. Clearly, if work is energy, work is needed to change the speed of a body in motion. More work is needed as the velocity increases. If an object of mass M moves with a velocity v, its energy is

$$K = \tfrac{1}{2} M v^2, \text{ unit} = kg \, m^2/s^2 = N \, m = \text{joule}.$$

This is called kinetic energy or energy of motion. The relationship between work and kinetic energy can be established by considering an example:

We found that the object starts from rest and when it passes $x_2 = 5m$ its velocity is $v = 2.45 m/s$

The kinetic energy of the block at x_2 is

$$K = \tfrac{1}{2} m v^2 = \tfrac{1}{2} (5 kg)(2.45 m/s)^2$$
$$= 15 \text{ joules}$$

We also found that the total work done by all forces that act on the block as it moves is

$$W_{TOTAL} = W_F + W_W + W_N + W_f = 15 \text{ joules}$$

So, in this example,

$$\boxed{W_{TOTAL} = K_f - K_i}$$

where $K_f = $ final kinetic energy $= \tfrac{1}{2} m v^2$
$$= 15 \text{ joules}$$
$$K_i = \text{initial kinetic energy} = 0$$

3.   The work-energy theorem.

$$W_{total} = K_{final} - K_{initial}.$$

This is a general result. For any system of moving masses, the total work done by all the forces that act on the masses as they move between two states of their motion is equal to their total kinetic energy in the second state minus their total kinetic energy in the initial state.

Example: a mass of 5 kg is projected upward from the surface of the earth with an initial speed of 25 m/s. Using the work-energy theorem, how high does it rise?

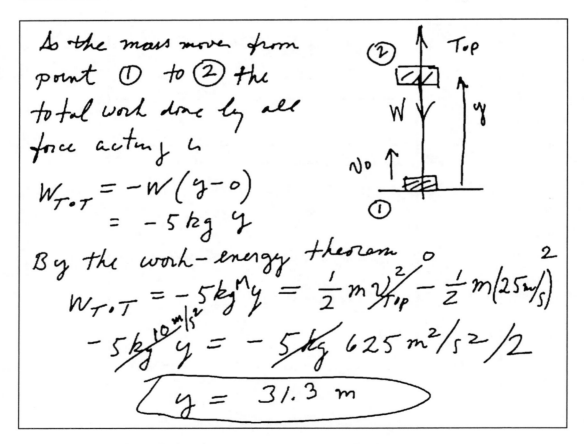

a) The Work-Energy Theorem and Potential Energy

$$W_{total} = K_{final} - K_{initial},$$

where

> W_{total} = the total work done by the forces acting on a system as it moves between two positions,
>
> K_{final} = the final kinetic energy of the system,
>
> $K_{initial}$ = the initial kinetic energy of the system.

Example. A 1 kg mass moves on a horizontal table top the is rough. Starting from rest, it is pulled to the right by a rope that goes over a pulley and attached to a ½ kg mass as shown below. What is the velocity of the system when the hanging mass drops 5 m ?

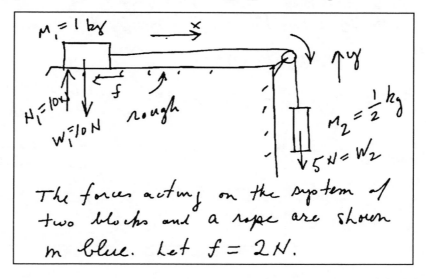

The total work done by the forces that act on the system of two blocks and a rope is:

$$W_{W_1} = W_{1x} \, 5m = 0(5) = 0$$

$$W_{N_1} = N_{1x} \, 5m = 0(5) = 0$$

$$W_f = (-2N)5m = -10 \text{ joules}$$

$+x$ in the direction of motion

$$W_{W_2} = W_{2y}(-5m) = -5N(-5m) = +25 \text{ joules}. \qquad y \text{ is down}$$

$$W_{TOTAL} = 0 + 0 - 10 + 25 = 15 \text{ joules}$$

The work-energy theorem gives the velocity after the system moves 5 m (the table block move 5 m the right, the hanging block moves 5 m downward, and they move together with the same speed):

$$W_{TOTAL} = k_f - k_i$$

$$k_f = \text{kinetic energy of the two blocks}$$

$$= \frac{1}{2} m_1 v^2 + \frac{1}{2} m_2 v^2$$

$$= \frac{1}{2} (1 kg) v^2 + \frac{1}{2} \left(\frac{1}{2} kg\right) v^2$$

$$= 0.75 \, kg \, v^2$$

$$k_i = 0 \qquad \text{both at rest initially}$$

$$W_{TOTAL} = 15 \text{ joules} = k_f - k_i = 0.75 \, kg \, v^2$$

$$v^2 = 15/.75 = 20 \, m^2/s^2 \rightarrow \boxed{v = 4.5 \, m/s}$$

b) Gravitational potential energy (energy of position).

A mass M = 1 kg is raised a distance of 2 m by an applied force F. It is moved to this height slowly so that the force F balances the weight W = M g.

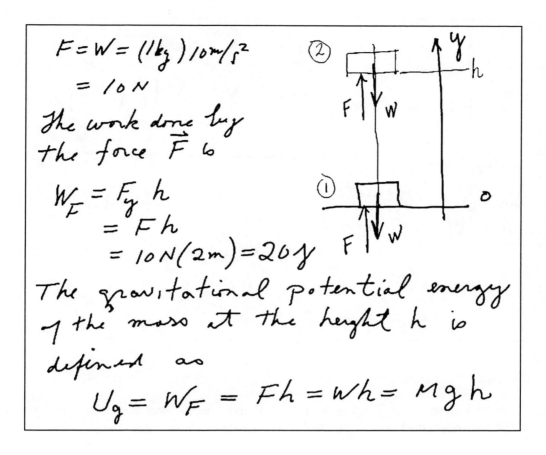

$$F = W = (1kg)10m/s^2$$
$$= 10N$$

The work done by the force $\vec{F}$ is

$$W_F = F_y \, h$$
$$= Fh$$
$$= 10N(2m) = 20J$$

The gravitational potential energy of the mass at the height h is defined as

$$U_g = W_F = Fh = Wh = Mgh$$

The work done against gravity to raise a mass M a distance h above the reference level (y=0) is called the gravitational potential energy:

$$U_g = M\,g\,h.$$

The gravitational potential energy is independent of the path used to raise a mass a distance h:

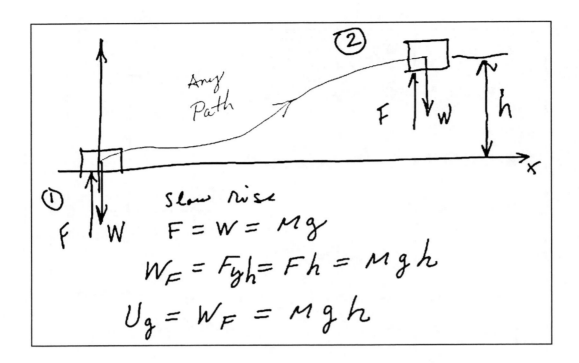

c) Mechanical energy and conservation of mechanical energy.

In the absence of friction the sum of the kinetic and the potential energy of a moving body is constant.

---

4.   Examples of conservation of energy.

The examples to be presented could be done using Newton's laws of motion. However, we will see that their solution is much more transparent and immediate by using the energy concept and conservation of energy.

a) Example 1.

An object of mass 5 kg is projected upward from the earth's surface with an initial velocity of 30 m/s. How high does it rise?

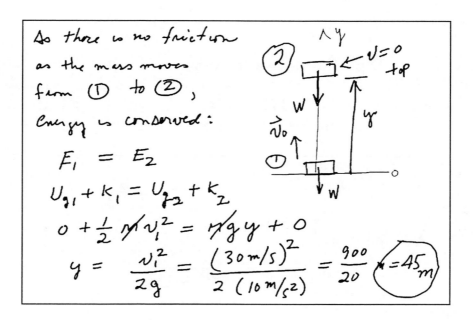

b) Example 2.

An object of mass 5 kg is at the top of an inclined plane at a height of 10 m. The plane is smooth and the length of the plane is 30 m. What is the velocity of the object when it reaches the bottom of the plane?

Distance from top to bottom along the plane = 30 m.

As there is no friction, energy is conserved.

$$E_1 = E_2$$

$$\tfrac{1}{2} m v_1^2 + m g y_1 = \tfrac{1}{2} m v_2^2 + m g (0)$$

$$0 + 5 kg (10 m/s^2)(10 m) = \tfrac{1}{2} 5 kg \, v_2^2$$

$$v_2^2 = 2(100 \, m^2/s^2) \rightarrow v_2 = \sqrt{200} \, m/s$$

$$= 14.14 \, m/s$$

c) Example 3. Over the hill.

A mass of 2 kg slides along a smooth curved surface starting at point "1" a height of 10 m with a velocity of 1 m/s. It moves as shown below and finally over a hill at point "2" which is at a height of 2 m. What is the speed of the mass as it passes over the point "2"?

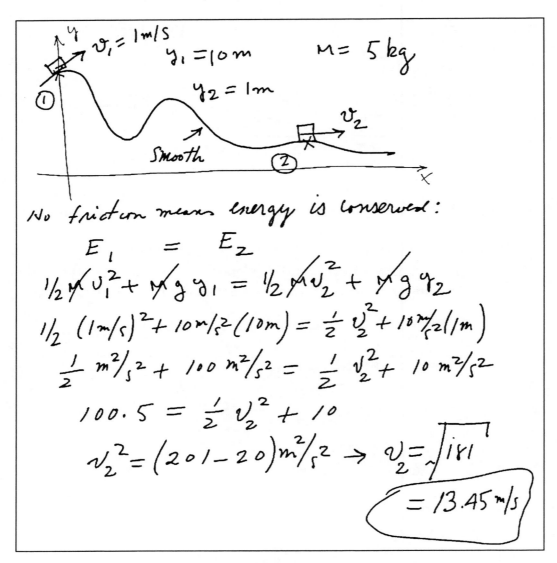

No friction means energy is conserved:

$$E_1 = E_2$$

$$\tfrac{1}{2} M v_1^2 + M g y_1 = \tfrac{1}{2} M v_2^2 + M g y_2$$

$$\tfrac{1}{2}(1 m/s)^2 + 10 m/s^2 (10 m) = \tfrac{1}{2} v_2^2 + 10 \tfrac{m}{s^2}(1 m)$$

$$\tfrac{1}{2} m^2/s^2 + 100 m^2/s^2 = \tfrac{1}{2} v_2^2 + 10 m^2/s^2$$

$$100.5 = \tfrac{1}{2} v_2^2 + 10$$

$$v_2^2 = (201 - 20) m^2/s^2 \rightarrow v_2 = \sqrt{181}$$

$$= 13.45 \, m/s$$

d) A loop-the-loop experiment with and without friction.

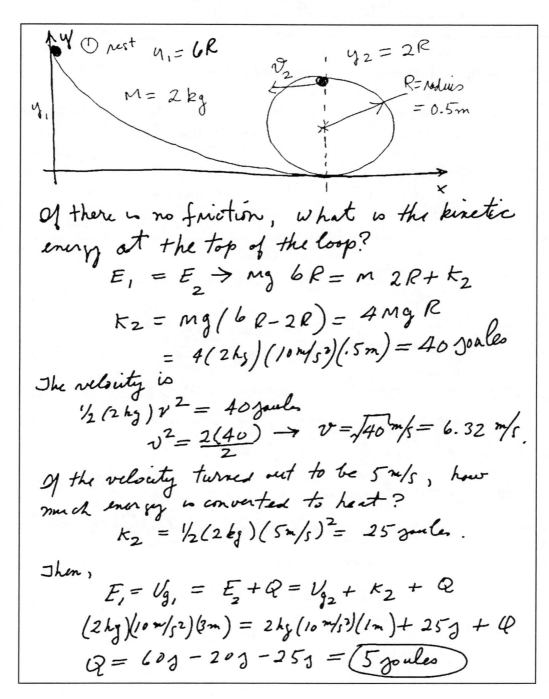

If there is no friction, what is the kinetic energy at the top of the loop?

$$E_1 = E_2 \rightarrow mg\, 6R = m\, 2R + k_2$$

$$k_2 = mg(6R - 2R) = 4MgR$$
$$= 4(2kg)(10 m/s^2)(.5m) = 40 \text{ joules}$$

The velocity is

$$\tfrac{1}{2}(2kg)v^2 = 40 \text{ joules}$$
$$v^2 = \frac{2(40)}{2} \rightarrow v = \sqrt{40} \, m/s = 6.32 \, m/s.$$

If the velocity turned out to be 5 m/s, how much energy is converted to heat?

$$k_2 = \tfrac{1}{2}(2kg)(5m/s)^2 = 25 \text{ joules}.$$

Then,

$$E_1 = U_{g_1} = E_2 + Q = U_{g_2} + k_2 + Q$$

$$(2kg)(10 m/s^2)(3m) = 2kg(10 m/s^2)(1m) + 25J + Q$$

$$Q = 60J - 20J - 25J = \boxed{5 \text{ joules}}$$

5.   What happens if there is friction?

a) Example of motion on a rough inclined plane.

Consider the problem where a mass of 5 kg slides down an inclined plane starting from rest at a height of 10 and sliding a distance of 30 m down the plane. If the surface of the plane is rough producing a friction force of 2 N on the mass, what is the velocity of the mass when it reaches the bottom. Recall that the velocity was 14.1 m/s when the plane was smooth.

So there is friction, energy is not conserved. However, we always have the work-energy theorem:

$$W_{total} = W_N + W_W + W_f$$
$$= 0 + (-W)(-10m) + (-2N)(30m)$$
$$= 50N(10m) - 2N(30m)$$
$$= 500 - 60 = 440 \text{ joules}$$

Thus
$$W_{total} = 440 \text{ joules} = K_f - K_i$$
$$= \frac{1}{2}mv_2^2 - 0$$
$$= \frac{1}{2}(5kg)v_2^2$$

$$\rightarrow v_2^2 = \frac{880}{5} = 176 \text{ m}^2/s^2 \rightarrow \boxed{v = 13.26 \text{ m/s}}$$

We see that friction has reduced the speed from 14.14 m/s to 13.26 m/s. Mechanical energy has been converted to heat:

$$\text{Energy converted to heat} = \frac{1}{2}(5 kg)(14.14 m/s)^2 - \frac{1}{2}(5 kg)(13.26 m/s)^2$$

$$= 60 \text{ joules}$$

Note

$$f \cdot 30 m = 2 N (30 m) = 60 \text{ joules}$$

b) Energy- Mechanical and Heat Energy

We revisit the last problem of a mass sliding down a rough inclined plane with the intent of finding how much energy is converted of to heat energy.

When there is no friction, mechanical energy is conserved, and

$$E_1 = E_2 \rightarrow Mg y_1 = \frac{1}{2} M v_2^2$$

$$v = 14.14 \text{ m/s}$$

When the plane is rough with $f = 2N$, we found by using the work-energy theorem that

$$v_2 = 13.26 \text{ m/s}.$$

We see that friction has reduced the speed from 14.14 m/s to 13.26 m/s. Mechanical energy has been converted to heat:

When the incline is rough,

$$E_2 - E_1 = \left(0 + \frac{1}{2} \, 5 \, kg \, (13.26 \, m/s)^2\right)$$
$$- (5 \, kg)(10 \, m/s^2)(10 \, m).$$
$$= 440 \text{ joules} - 500 \text{ J}$$
$$= -60 \text{ joules}$$

Mechanical energy is lost. Where does it go?

$$W_f = (-2 N)(30 m) = -60 \text{ joules}$$

Friction takes 60 joules away from the system whose original energy was $mg \, y_1 = 500$ joules leaving 440 joules.

---

6.   Conservation of momentum

Before we leave this important chapter on energy and its conservation, let's return to the concept of momentum

$$P = M v$$

that was introduced in connection with Newton's second law of motion. We said that the correct form of Newton's law must be that the net force acting on a mass M is not $F = M a$. The law must be

$$F = \Delta P / \Delta t.$$

The force is equal to the rate of change of momentum of the system.

a) A system of interacting particles and conservation of momentum.

If a system consists of many interacting particles, then they exert forces on each other. In addition, there may also be external forces that act on this system. The forces between the particles come in action-reaction pairs, so when these are added together vectorially, they cancel. This means that Newton's law becomes

$$F = F_{internal} + F_{external} = \Delta P / \Delta t.$$

Here, the internal forces are the sum of the action-reaction pairs, and $F_{internal} = 0$. If there are no external forces, then

$$\Delta P / \Delta t = 0.$$

This means that the momentum of the system does not change, and this is a statement of the conservation of the momentum of the system:

$$P = \text{constant for no external forces.}$$

b) Explanation of the executive toy.

The toy that we have seen demonstrated is explained by using both conservation of energy and conservation of momentum.

- Two balls with equal mass.

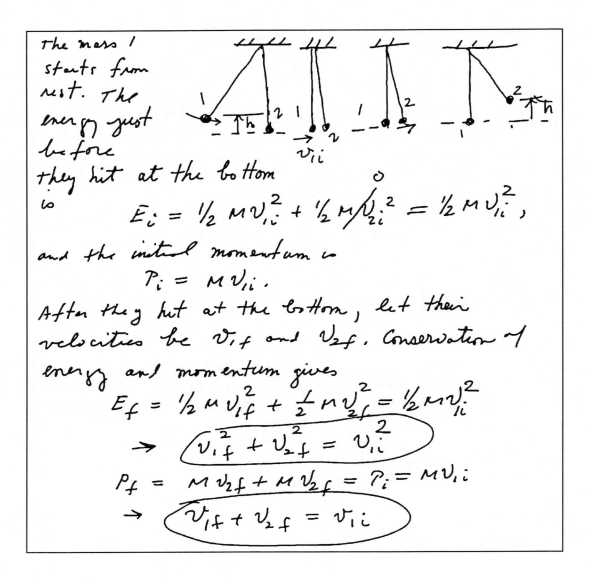

The mass 1 starts from rest. The energy just before they hit at the bottom is

$$E_i = \tfrac{1}{2} M v_{1i}^2 + \tfrac{1}{2} M v_{2i}^2 = \tfrac{1}{2} M v_{1i}^2,$$

and the initial momentum is

$$P_i = M v_{1i}.$$

After they hit at the bottom, let their velocities be v_{1f} and v_{2f}. Conservation of energy and momentum gives

$$E_f = \tfrac{1}{2} M v_{1f}^2 + \tfrac{1}{2} M v_{2f}^2 = \tfrac{1}{2} M v_{1i}^2$$

$$\Rightarrow \quad \boxed{v_{1f}^2 + v_{2f}^2 = v_{1i}^2}$$

$$P_f = M v_{2f} + M v_{2f} = P_i = M v_{1i}$$

$$\Rightarrow \quad \boxed{v_{1f} + v_{2f} = v_{1i}}$$

If we take the circled equations and put them together, the result is

$$v_{1f}^2 + v_{1f}^2 = v_{1f}^2 = v_{1f}^2 + v_{1f}^2 + 2\, v_{1f}\, v_{1f} \rightarrow v_{1f}\, v_{1f} = 0.$$

But v_{1f} cannot be zero as it absorbs the shock of being struck, so $v_{1f} = 0$. This in turn means that $v_{1f} = v_{1f}$. The second particle takes all of the energy of the collision while the first particle stops dead in its tracks. This is an example of how physics can predict a result that may be entirely unexpected. In its domain, physics is king.

- Three balls with equal mass.

In the same way, if we have a toy with three balls and pull two over and then release them, the first ball will stop dead in its tracks and the other two will move off together as shown below. The analysis is done by requiring that momentum and energy are conserved.

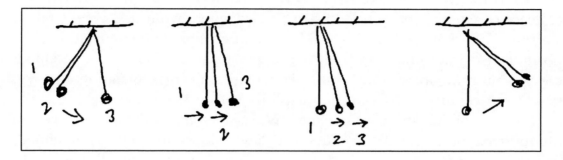

CHAPTER 7

Thermodynamics

We have moved from Newton's laws of motion and gravitation to the concept of energy, and this led us to a place where we found energy taking another form that is not mechanical. Friction changes energy of motion and position to some other form. Heat energy can in fact be related to kinetic energy, but it involves other forms like radiation energy. Radiation energy is nineteenth-century stuff and involves the electromagnetic field. So our conception of reality is enlarging. We will start with the subject of thermodynamics, and introduce more laws of nature. They will indeed enlarge our view of nature and of time. The "arrow of time" will be the result of the second law of thermodynamics.

1. Temperature Scales.

a) The Kelvin scale.

The temperature of a gas in a closed container is related to the total mechanical energy of the molecules in within. The temperature of the gas in the Absolute or Kelvin scale (T) is

$$K_{\text{average of gas molecules}} = 3/2\,k\,T,$$
$$k = \text{Boltzmann constant} = 1.381 \times 10^{-23}\ \text{joules/K}$$

where the temperature T has the unit called K (for Kelvin). The temperature K = 0 corresponds to absolute zero where the molecules are at rest. The temperature of the universe is 2.7 K because the universe is in motion.

The Kelvin Scale

universe 10^{-12} sec old 10^{16}

                                            5×10^{8} universe at 3 min

interior of sun 10^{7}

                                            6000 temp of surface of sun

water boils   373

                                            273.15 water freezes

coldest temp   185
on earth
                                            4.2 liquid helium

                                            2.7 K background universe

0 ——————————— Absolute zero

b) The Centigrade scale.

$$t_c = T - 273.15 \, ,$$

T = temperature in kelvin

t_c = temp. in centigrade

t_c (freezing water) = $0 \,^{\circ}C$

t_c (boiling water) = $100 \,^{\circ}C$

c) The Fahrenheit scale.

$$t_f = \frac{9}{5} T - 459.67$$

$$t_f = \frac{9}{5} t_c + 32.0$$

$$t_f (\text{freezing water}) = \frac{9}{5}(0) + 32.0$$
$$= 32.0 \text{ }^\circ F$$

$$t_f (\text{boiling water}) = \frac{9}{5}(100) + 32$$
$$= 212.0 \text{ }^\circ F$$

$$t_f = 70 \text{ }^\circ F \implies t_c = (t_f - 32)\frac{5}{9} = 22.2 \text{ }^\circ c$$

---

2. Heat energy.

If an amount of heat Q is added to a body of mass M, its temperature will increase. The temperature will be raised by an amount ΔT, and

$$Q = c \, M \, \Delta T,$$

where c = the specific heat of the substance,

$$\Delta T = T_{final} - T_{initial}.$$

Heat energy Q enters the substance, for example by friction, and raises the temperature

$$\Delta T = \Delta t_c = t_{final} - t_{initial}$$

This change is related to Q as

$$Q = c M \Delta T.$$

c = specific heat of the substance.

The unit of Q is joule, so the unit of c is joule/(kg K)= joule/(kg C).

a) Specific heat of various substances:

Iron: c = 502 joules/kg C,
Aluminum: c = 900 joules/kg C,
Copper: c = 385 joules/kg C,
Ice: c = 2090 joules/kg C,
Water: c = 4186 joules/kg C,
Air: c = 1000 J/kg C.

b) Example 1.

The brakes on a car are made of iron of total mass 10 kg. The car of total mass 1000 kg (including the brakes) moves with a velocity of 20 m/s, and it brakes to rest. If the temperature of the brakes is 20 C before they are applied, what is their temperature just after the care stops?

$$W_{friction} = K_f - K_i = 0 - \frac{1}{2}(1000 \, kg)(20 \, m/s)^2$$

$$= -200,000 \text{ joules}$$

Then produced heat q that raises the temperature of the brakes:

$$q = C_{un} M (t_c - 20°c)$$

$$= 502 \frac{joule}{kg°c} (10 \, kg)(t_c - 20°c)$$

$$200,000 \, J = 502 \frac{joule}{°c} (10) \, t_c - 100,400 \text{ joules}$$

$$t_c = \frac{(200,000 + 100,400) J}{5020 \, J/°c} = \boxed{59.8 \, °C}$$

The brakes have a temperature of $t_f = 9/5(59.8) + 32 = 140$ f.

c) Example 2.

A pail of water at 20 C has a mass of 10 kg. A 1 kg piece of copper at a temperature of 150 C is dropped into the pail, and the system comes to an equilibrium temperature of t_c. Assuming that no energy is lost, what is t_c?

Energy is conserved, so

$$Q_{cu} + Q_{H_2O} = 0$$

$$C_{cu} M_{cu} (t_c - 150°c) + C_{H_2O} M_{H_2O} (t_c - 20°c) = 0$$

$$385 \frac{J}{kg°c} (1 \, kg)(t_c - 150c) + 4186 \frac{J}{kg°c} (10 \, kg)$$

$$\times (t_c - 20°c) = 0$$

$$(385 + 41860) t_c - (57750 + 837200) = 0$$

$$t_c = \frac{894950}{42245} = \boxed{21.2 \, °c}$$

3.　The zero and first laws of thermodynamics.

a) The zero law.

If two objects A and B are in thermal equilibrium with a third object C, the A and B are in equilibrium with each other. Equilibrium means they are at the same temperature.

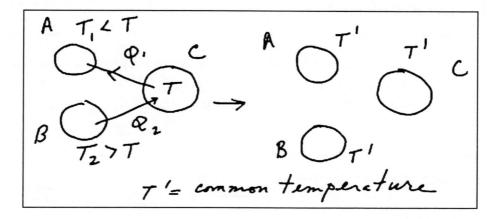

b) The first law.

We first define the internal energy of a substance

$$U = \text{total energy content of a substance by itself.}$$

For simple substances such as gases, the internal energy is directly related to the absolute temperature of the gas, which in turn is related to the kinetic energy of the particles in the gas. Then, an increase in the internal energy of a substance ΔU is equal to the **heat (Q) added** plus the **work done on the system (W):**

$$\Delta U = W + Q.$$

This is the first law.

- Example 1: during a thermodynamic process, 28 J of heat are added and the system expands doing 12 J of work. What is the the change in the internal energy of the system?

$$\Delta U = W + Q$$
$$= 12 J + 28 J = 40 J.$$
The internal energy (temperature) increases.

- Example 2: an insulated cylinder containing air is confined by piston that is pushed by a force of 10 N so that the piston moves 25 cm inward. What is the change in the internal energy of the gas?

Insulated means
$$Q = 0.$$
$$W = F \times distance$$
$$= 10 N (.25 m)$$
$$= +2.5 J$$
First law:
$$\Delta U = W + Q = 2.5 J + 0 = 2.5 J$$
The temperature of the gas increases.

gas ← F = 10 N
insulation

c) Phase change.

If heat is added to a substance, its temperature will rise according to

$$Q = c M (T_{final} - T_{initial}),$$

where c is the specific heat of the substance, M is its mass and (T_{final} − $T_{initial}$), is the change in the absolute temperature of the substance. This change in temperature is equal to the change in the centigrade temperature.

If a substance is at the threshold of a phase change, either solid to liquid or liquid to gas, the addition of heat energy will not raise the temperature until the phase change is completed. The amount if heat energy need to produce a complete phase change is

$$Q = L M,$$

where L is the latent heat for the substance. Its unit is j/kg.

- Example 1. How much heat is required to convert 400 g of ice at −5 C to water at 5 C? We first note the following constants:

  L_{ice} = 79.8 cal/g = 79.8 × 10^3 cal/kg = 334 × 10^3 J/kg,
  L_{steam} = 2.357 × 10^6 J/kg,
  c_{ice} = 2090 J/kg C, c_{water} = 4186 J/kg C,
  4.186 J = 1 cal (calorie),
  1000 cal = 1 Cal (food calorie).

Bring ice to the melting temp. of $0°C$:
$$Q_1 = c_{ice} M_{ice} (0°c - (-5°c))$$
$$= 2090 \, ^J/_{kg°C} (.4kg)(5°c)$$
$$= 4180 \, J$$

Melt the ice :

$$Q_2 = L_{ice} M_{ice} = 334 \times 10^3 \frac{J}{kg} \cdot 4 kg$$

$$= 133.3 \times 10^3 J$$

Warm the water to 5°C :

$$Q_3 = C_{water} M_{water} (5°c - 0°c)$$

$$= 4186 \frac{J}{kg \cdot °c} (.4 kg)(5°c)$$

$$= 8372 \ J$$

$$\rightarrow Q_{TOTAL} = 4180 J + 133,300 J + 8372 J$$

$$\boxed{= 146 \times 10^3 \ J}$$

- Example 2. An insulated container of 1 kg of water at a temperature of 20 C is cooled by placing 200 g of ice at 0 C into the container. What is the final temperature of the mixture?

$$Q_{ice} + Q_{H_2O} = 0$$

$$Q_{ice} = Q_{melt\ it} + Q_{heat\ it}$$

$$= L_{ice}\ M_{ice}$$

$$+ C_{water \atop from\ ice}\ M_{water \atop from\ ice}\ (t_c - 0^\circ c)$$

$$= 334 \times 10^3\ J/kg\ (.2kg) + 4186\ \frac{J}{kg\ ^\circ c}\ (.2kg)$$
$$\times (t_c - 0^\circ)$$

$$= 66.8 \times 10^3\ J$$
$$+ 837.2\ \frac{J}{^\circ c}\ t_c$$

$$Q_{H_2O} = C_{H_2O}\ M_{H_2O}\ (t_c - 20^\circ c)$$

$$= 4186\ \frac{J}{kg\ ^\circ c}\ (1kg)(t_c - 20^\circ c)$$

$$= 4186\ \frac{J}{^\circ c}\ t_c - 83720\ J$$

$$Q_{ice} + Q_{H_2O} = 66.8 \times 10^3\ J + 837.2\ \frac{J}{^\circ c}\ t_c$$
$$+ 4186\ \frac{J}{^\circ c}\ t_c - 83720\ J = 0$$

$$t_c = \frac{-66,800 + 83720}{4186 + 837.2}\ ^\circ c = \boxed{3.4^\circ C}$$

4.   The second law of thermodynamics.

a) A heat engine.

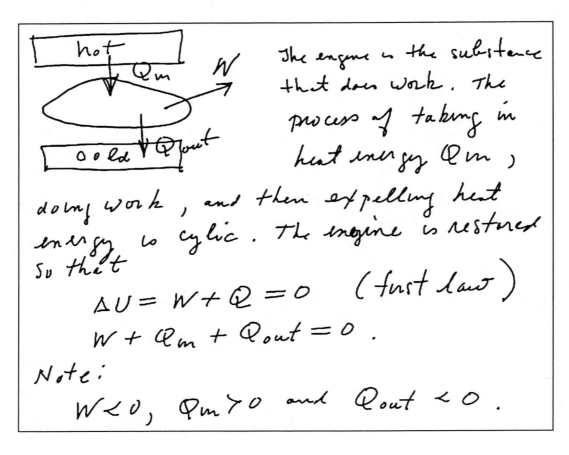

The engine is the substance that does work. The process of taking in heat energy Q_{in}, doing work, and then expelling heat energy is cyclic. The engine is restored so that

$$\Delta U = W + Q = 0 \quad (\text{first law})$$
$$W + Q_{in} + Q_{out} = 0.$$

Note:
$$W < 0, \quad Q_{in} > 0 \quad \text{and} \quad Q_{out} < 0.$$

b) The second law in its first form.

It is impossible to build a heat engine that performs mechanical work on its surroundings and does not exhaust heat energy into its surroundings. That is, Q_{out} cannot be zero.

The efficiency of a heat engine is

$$\eta = |W|/Q_{in}.$$

The maximum efficiency of a heat engine is from a "Carnot" engine, and it is $(1 - T_{cold}/T_{hot})$.

Example. How much work is done by an engine that takes in 2000 J of heat and exhausts 800 J of heat? What is its efficiency?

$$Q_{in} + Q_{out} + W = 0$$

$$2000\,J - 800\,J + W = 0$$

$$W = 800\,J - 2000\,J = \boxed{-1200\,J}$$

$$\eta = \frac{|W|}{Q_{in}} = \frac{1200\,J}{2000\,J} = \boxed{0.6}$$

c) The second law in its second form.

It is impossible to build a refrigerator that can transfer heat from a low-temperature region to a high-temperature region without using mechanical work.

- Example 1.

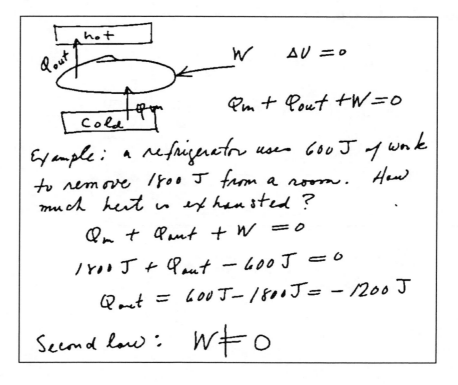

hot

Q_{out}

W $\Delta U = 0$

Cold Q_{in}

$$Q_{in} + Q_{out} + W = 0$$

Example: a refrigerator uses 600 J of work to remove 1800 J from a room. How much heat is exhausted?

$$Q_{in} + Q_{out} + W = 0$$

$$1800\,J + Q_{out} - 600\,J = 0$$

$$Q_{out} = 600\,J - 1800\,J = -1200\,J$$

Second law: $W \neq 0$

- Example 2.

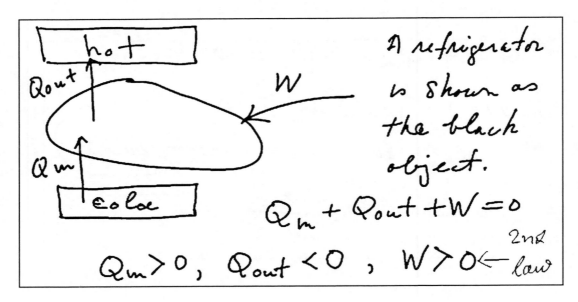

A refrigerator is shown as the black object.

$$Q_{in} + Q_{out} + W = 0$$

$$Q_{in} > 0, \quad Q_{out} < 0, \quad W > 0 \leftarrow \text{2nd law}$$

Example: a refrigerator uses 600 J of work to remove 1800 J from a room. How much heat is exhausted?

$$Q_{in} + Q_{out} + W = 0$$

$$1800\,J + Q_{out} + 600\,J = 0$$

$$Q_{out} = -(1800 + 600)\,J = -2400\,J$$

COP = coefficient of performance

$$= Q_{in}/W = 1800/600 = 3$$

d) It is impossible to build a perpetual motion machine.

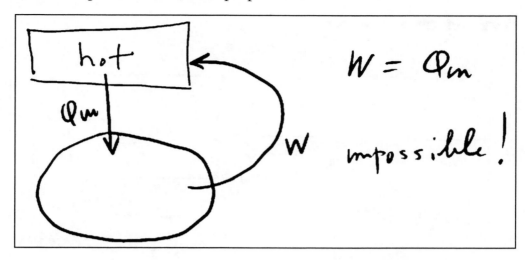

5.   The arrow of time and the third law.

This form of the second law of thermodynamics is actually the one from which the others can be derived, so it is the most general expression of the law. It states that isolated systems tend to change in the direction of decreasing order.

a) Entropy.

The thermodynamic arrow of time means that in a closed system, movement in time in is the direction of decreasing order or increasing entropy. The quantity called entropy either stays the same or increases. A change in entropy is defined as ΔS = heat transferred within the system/ Temperature of the system.
In a statistical sense, entropy is a measure of the order of the system, where small means high order and S large means low order[8]. Low order means there are many more available states for the system. The second law of thermodynamics can be expressed as $\Delta S > 0$ or 0.

---

[8] Ludwig Boltzmann showed that the second law means that an isolated system moves in time in the direction of increasing entropy or increasing disorder. This work was completed near the end of the nineteeth century. It is the first time that probabilities were shown to play a foundational role in physics.

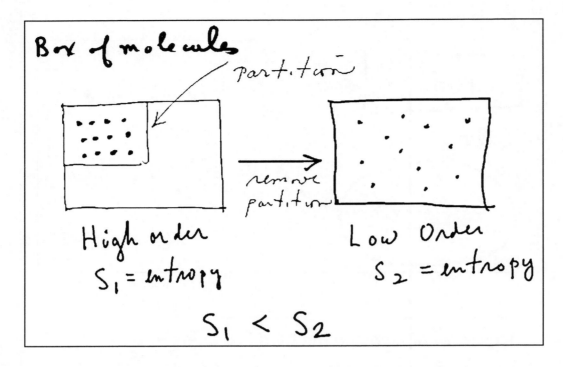

b) The psychological arrow of time.

If memory could move in a direction opposite the thermodynamic arrow of time, then we could remember the future.

However, human memory, like computer memory, involves organizing memory units into an ordered state from a disordered state. So, memory units increase their state of order, and that means their entropy decreases. This comes about at the expense of energy from the surrounding space, and the overall effect is an increase in the overall entropy. The total effect is an increase in entropy for the memory-surrounding space system. Therefore, even when we are learning and increasing information within ourselves, the direction of memory follows the thermodynamic arrow of time.

CHAPTER 8

Waves

The rest of this and the next course will look at physics from the point of waves. This encompasses such topics and harmonic oscillators (springs), traveling waves on strings, sound, electric and magnetic waves and quantum mechanics. Before we end this term, we will begin the discussion with harmonic motion and waves on a string. The point of view is much different than the particle approach, as waves are not defined at a point, but they exist over space.

1.	The harmonic wave and simple harmonic motion.

a) Generation of harmonic motion.

Consider the motion of a point in a circle and it projection of the y axis as shown below. It is the motion of a mass on a spring, called simple harmonic motion.

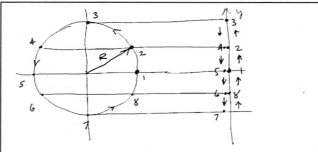

The circular motion which is counter-clockwise starting at $1 \to 2 \to \cdots \to 7 \to 8$. When projected on the y axis, the motion is up $1 \to 2 \to 3 \cdot 4$ then down $4 \to 5 \to 6, 7$, then up $7 \to 8$. It then repeats. The mathematic representation is

$$y = R \sin(\omega t), \qquad \omega = \text{angular frequency}$$

$$R = \text{radius}$$

b) The harmonic sine wave stretched out along the time axis.

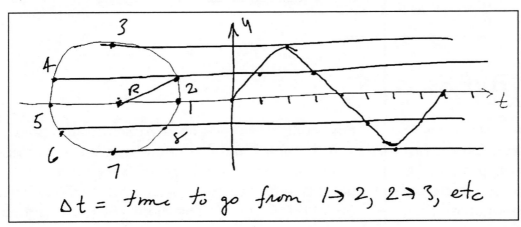

$$\Delta t = \text{time to go from } 1 \to 2, \ 2 \to 3, \text{ etc}$$

c) Properties of the sine wave in time.

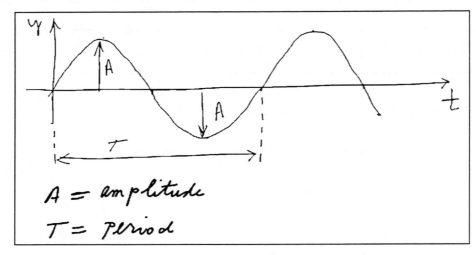

A = amplitude

T = period

d) A sine wave along the x-axis.

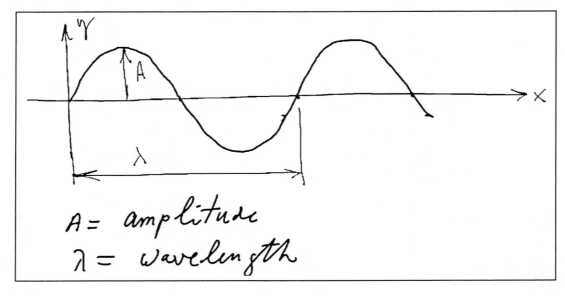

A = amplitude

λ = wavelength

e) A sine wave traveling along the x-axis observed at a fixed point on the axis.

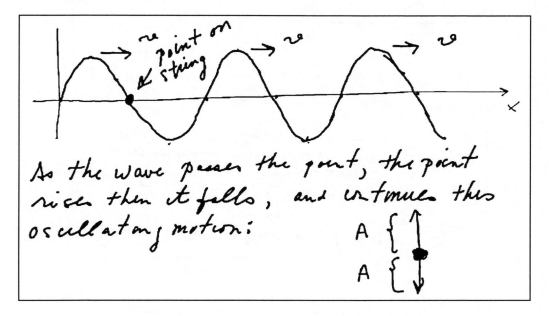

As the wave passes the point, the point rises then it falls, and continues this oscillating motion:

A {↑}
A {↓}

The wave moves a distance of one wavelength in a time T, so the speed of the wave is

$$v = \frac{distance}{time} = \frac{\lambda}{T} = \frac{\lambda}{1/f}$$

$$\boxed{v = f\lambda}$$

f) Example.

A traveling wave on a string with a speed of 2 m/s makes a point on the string bob up and down over a vertical distance of 30 cm from the top of its path to the bottom of its path twice each second. What is the period, wavelength and amplitude of the wave?

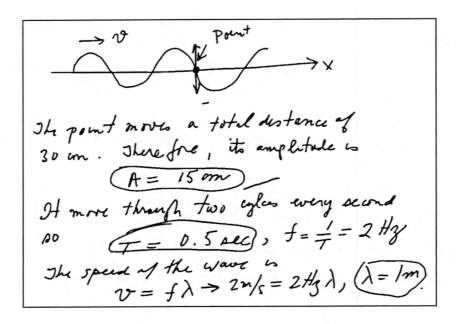

The point moves a total distance of
30 cm. Therefore, its amplitude is
$$A = 15 \text{ cm}$$
It moves through two cycles every second
so $T = 0.5 \text{ sec}$, $f = \frac{1}{T} = 2 \text{ Hz}$
The speed of the wave is
$$v = f\lambda \rightarrow 2m/s = 2Hz\,\lambda, \quad \lambda = 1m.$$

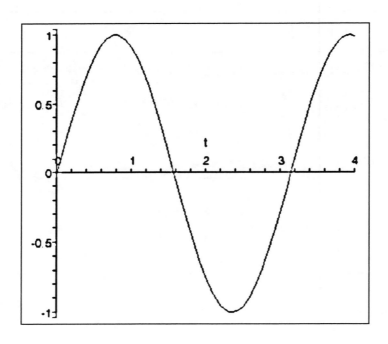

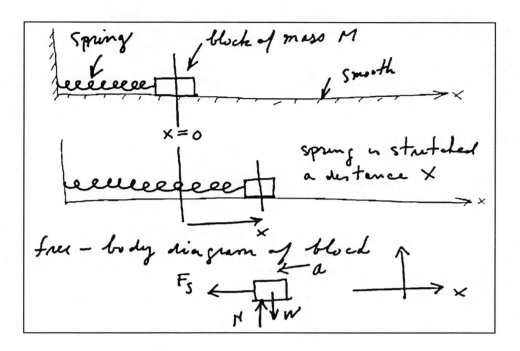

2. The simple harmonic oscillator.

a) The spring oscillator.

The spring force Fs = k x, k = spring constant (unit = N/m), and it is the only force in the x direction causing an acceleration a:

$$\Sigma F_x = -kx = ma$$

$$a = -\frac{k}{m}x, \quad x = \text{stretch of spring from equilibrium.}$$

The motion of an object with acceleration

$$a = -k/m \, x \quad \text{is}$$

$$x = A \sin(\omega t)$$

where

$$\omega = 2\pi f = \sqrt{k/m} \rightarrow \boxed{f = \frac{1}{T} = \frac{1}{2\pi}\sqrt{\frac{k}{m}}}$$

55

a) $T = 1\sec = \dfrac{1}{f} = 2\pi\sqrt{\dfrac{m}{k}} = \dfrac{2\pi\sqrt{.5\,kg}}{\sqrt{k}}$

$\rightarrow k = \dfrac{4\pi^2(.5\,kg)}{1\sec^2} = \boxed{19.7\ N/m}$

b) $m = 1\,kg,\quad k = 19.7\ N/m,$

$T = 2\pi\sqrt{m/k} = 2\pi\sqrt{\dfrac{1\,kg}{19.7\ N/m}} = 1.4\ \sec$

$f = \dfrac{1}{T} = \dfrac{1}{1.4}\sec^{-1} = 0.71\ Hz$

c) These equation do not involve g, so there is no difference on the moon.

$T = 2\pi\sqrt{\dfrac{L}{g}}\ \sec = 1\ \sec$

$4\pi^2\,L/g = 1\ \sec^2$

$L = \dfrac{(1\sec^2)(9.8\ m/s^2)}{4\pi^2} = 2.43\ m.$

On the moon where $g_{moon} = 1.6\ m/s^2$, this length would have a period of

$T_{moon} = 2\pi\sqrt{\dfrac{2.43\,m}{1.6\,m/s^2}} = 7.7\ \sec$

---

b) The spring clock.

A mass of 500 g is attached to a spring of constant k = 50 N/m. The relaxed length of the spring is 50 cm. It the oscillator is allowed to settle to an equilibrium position, how far below this position does it settle to rest? The mass is then pulled downward an additional 5 cm and released. Find the period, frequency and amplitude of the subsequent simple-harmonic motion?

The mass is pulled down 5 cm. It will oscillate about $y=0$ with

$$A = 5 \text{ cm} = \boxed{0.05 \text{ m}}$$

The period

$$T = 2\pi \sqrt{\frac{M}{k}} = 2\pi \sqrt{\frac{.5 \text{ kg}}{50 \text{ N/m}}} = \boxed{0.63 \text{ s}}$$

and

$$f = \frac{1}{T} = \boxed{1.6 \text{ Hz}}.$$

c) The pendulum clock.

$$\Sigma F_x = -T\frac{x}{L} = Ma, \quad \theta \text{ small} < 10°$$

$$\Sigma F_y = T - W = 0$$

$$a = -\frac{Tx}{LM} = \frac{-Mgx}{LM} = -\frac{g}{L}x$$

Recall for a spring,

$$a = -\frac{k}{M}x$$
$$\rightarrow T = 2\pi\sqrt{\frac{M}{k}}.$$

By analogy, the period of a pendulum is

$$T = 2\pi\sqrt{\frac{L}{g}}.$$

A clock maker is making a pendulum clock with period of 1 second. How long does the pendulum have to be? But the rod turns out to be 1 mm too long. How much time will the clock gain or lose in one day?

$$T = 1 \text{ sec} = 2\pi \sqrt{L/g} = 2\pi \sqrt{L/9.8 \text{ m/s}^2}$$

$$\rightarrow \quad 1 \text{ sec}^2 = 4\pi^2 L /(9.8 \text{ m/s}^2)$$

$$L = 9.8 /(4\pi^2) = \boxed{0.2482 \text{ m}}$$

$$\text{If} \quad L = 0.2482 \text{ m} + 0.001 \text{ m} = 0.2492 \text{ m},$$

then

$$T = 2\pi \sqrt{L/g} = 2\pi \sqrt{\frac{.2492 \text{ m}}{9.8 \text{ m/s}^2}} = 1.002 \text{ sec}$$

$$1 \text{ day} = 86,400 \text{ sec}$$

$$\text{number of clicks in a day} = \frac{86,400}{1.002} = 86228$$

$$\rightarrow \text{The clock will lose } 86,400 - 86228$$
$$= \boxed{172 \text{ sec} = 2.87 \text{ min}}$$

---

3.   The Interference of Waves.

This discussion begins a reach into the modern world of physics.

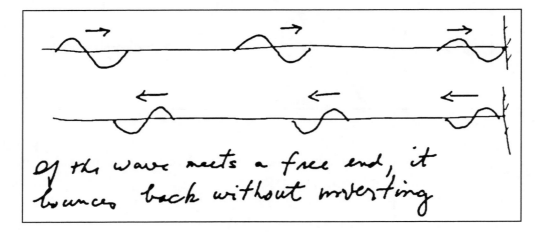

If the wave meets a free end, it bounces back without inverting

Particles interact and produce changes of motion in each other by virtue of forces and accelerations. They move in definite trajectories that can be drawn as lines in three-dimensional space. Waves, on the other hand fill space, and their interactions involve patterns in space where some portions are filled with wave activity and other portions are devoid of wave activity. The picture of a physical reality expressed in terms of waves loses local concentration and becomes global or extended. We will follow this line of thought through more classical ideas including the huge subject of electromagnetism, and we will eventually arrive at a strange but more accurate world view depicted by quantum mechanics.

The first and perhaps most important thing to grasp is the idea of discrete states as exemplified by standing waves. We need to explore wave interference to get to this point.

a) Constructive and destructive interference.

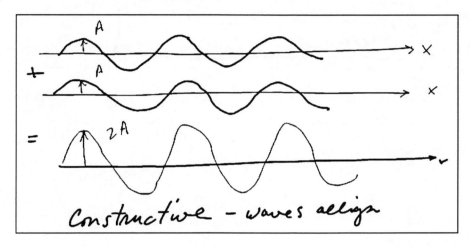

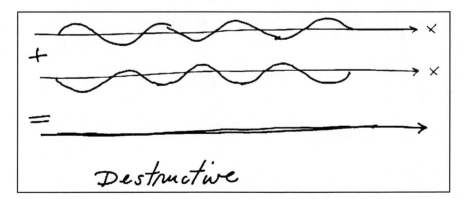

The interference of two harmonic traveling waves moving in opposite directions results in the formation of standing waves.

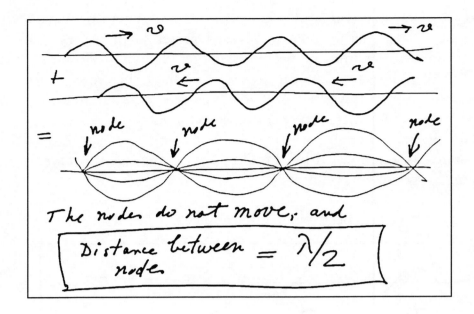

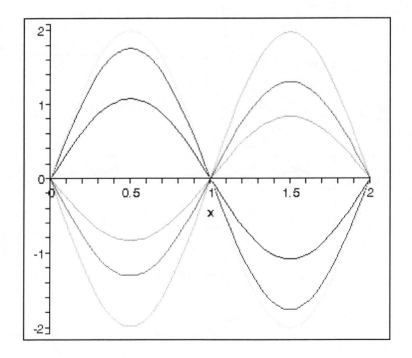

b) Standing waves on a string that is tied at both ends.

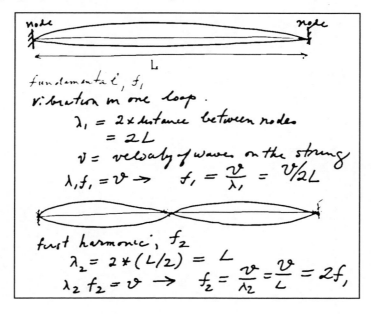

node   node

L

fundamental, f_1
vibration in one loop.
$\lambda_1 = 2 \times$ distance between nodes
$= 2L$
$v =$ velocity of waves on the string
$\lambda_1 f_1 = v \Rightarrow \quad f_1 = \dfrac{v}{\lambda_1} = \dfrac{v}{2L}$

first harmonic, f_2
$\lambda_2 = 2 \ast (L/2) = L$
$\lambda_2 f_2 = v \Rightarrow \quad f_2 = \dfrac{v}{\lambda_2} = \dfrac{v}{L} = 2f_1$

$f_3 =$ second harmonic
$\lambda_3 = 2(L/3) = \tfrac{2}{3}L$
$f_3 \lambda_3 = v \Rightarrow \quad f_3 = \dfrac{v}{\lambda_3} = \dfrac{3v}{2L}$
$\qquad\qquad = 3f_1$
In general, $\quad f_n = n f_1, \quad n = 1, 2, \cdots$
where $\quad n = 1$ is the fundamental

- Example: A rope 3m long is tied at both ends. The speed of waves on the rope is 18 m/s. What are the possible frequencies of the standing waves on this rope?

$\lambda_1 = 2(L) = 6m$
$f_1 = \dfrac{v}{\lambda_1} = \dfrac{18\,m/s}{6m} = 3\,Hz$
$f_2 = 2f_1 = (6\,Hz)$
$f_3 = 3f_1 = 9\,Hz) \quad \cdots$

Light, Optics, & Electricity

Introduction to the Second Course

The first physics course was mainly concerned with particles moving under the influence of forces governed by Newton's laws of motion. We studied motion in one and two dimensions accelerated by forces. Particles were for the most part regarded as points of matter localized in space, and they move in continuous paths in space. Space and time were assumed to be absolute, independent of each other and independent of matter.

We introduced the idea of work done by a force and energy – energy of motion (kinetic energy) and energy of position (potential energy). We also noted that frictional forces convert kinetic and potential energy into heat, and this in turn led to thermodynamics and its first two laws. The second law gives a direction to time – the arrow of time.

The first course ended with a discussion of waves. In particular, we discussed and demonstrated waves on a string, both traveling waves and standing waves. Waves represent another way of describing physical reality. A wave exists in space, and it is extended and not a point phenomenon. This means that the energy associated with waves also extends over space.

Waves interact with each other, but not through forces as particles do. They interact by interfering with each other, and two waves, each having energy content, can annihilate each other to produce nothing, or they can reinforce each other to produce a more energetic wave. The wave nature of entities in the world as we know it leads to a much different view of experimental observation. Ultimately, the wave nature of particles leads to a totally new view of what can be understood about the world. The modern worldview calculates probabilities for the particular results of measurements rather than supplying a picture. The clockwork universe disappears and it is replaced by a world of possibilities each carrying its own probability for existing.

So, we will turn our attention to a wave picture of reality, starting where we left off last term. Hearing and seeing are two of our most important senses, and each is a human response to the environment in which we find ourselves. We will start with sound and discuss its wave nature, and then we will move to light and its wave nature. Understanding these phenomenon have led to technological innovations of great importance to the human condition including language, music, painting, photography and all of the graphic arts.

Once we have explored waves, we can turn to the second greatest component of the classical era following mechanics. This is the discovery and understanding of electricity and magnetism[9]. With knowledge of mechanics and electromagnetism, we have the intellectual tools to appreciate the dilemma confronting physics at the turn of the twentieth century, and we will see that the resolution led to a paradigm shift to the theories of relativity and quantum mechanics. The notion of absolute space and time topple, and the picture of objects moving along paths fades.

---

[9] Electric and magnetic phenomena were studied and set into theory for more than a century by many people, including Benjamin Franklin. The Scottish physicist James Clark Maxwell discovered a beautiful synthesis of the phenomena of electricity and magnetism in a set of equations now and forever baring his name. This work extended from about 1860 to his death in 1879 and can be explored in the book "The Scientific Papers of James Clark Maxwell by himself (Dover, 1965).

CHAPTER 9

Waves and Sound

Sound is a pressure wave. By this is meant that it needs a medium in which to exist, it is a train of high and low pressure spaces that move through the medium with a speed that depends on the medium. For example sound waves in air at normal conditions, like ground level on a warm day, have a speed of 343 m/s. The spectrum of frequencies for humans who are young and of excellent health is 20 Hz to 20,000 Hz. The energy content of a sound wave is measured by the amount of energy that passes a point per unit area and per unit time. This quantity is called the intensity of the sound wave, and its unit is watts/meter^2. The average threshold of hearing, again for young and healthy humans, is 10^{-12} watts/m^2. The threshold of pain is 1 watt/m^2.

1. The physical parameters.

a) The harmonic wave for a pure tone.

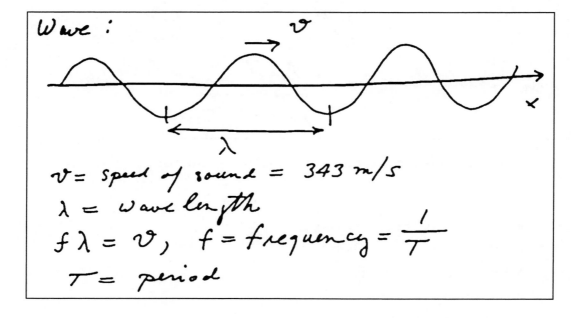

b) Standing waves and the decibel.

Standing wave — interference of two traveling waves moving in opposite directions:

Distance between nodes = $\lambda/2$

String tied at both ends:

$$f_n = n f_1 \quad , \quad f_1 = \text{fundamental}.$$
$$= v/2L$$

Intensity level:

$I = \text{intensity} = $ Energy of wave as it passes per second and per unit area

$$= \frac{\text{Joules}}{\text{sec } m^2} = \frac{\text{watts}}{m^2}$$

Human range $\dfrac{10^{-12} \text{ watts}}{m^2} \longrightarrow \dfrac{1 \text{ watt}}{m^2}$

threshold   pain

$$\text{Intensity level} = 10 \log I/I_0 \ db$$
$$\underbrace{\qquad}_{\text{power of ten}}$$

The decibel is a convenient measure of the intensity of the wave. For example:

- Threshold of hearing = 0 db
- Rustling leaves = 10 db
- A mosquito = 40 db
- Normal convesation = 60 db
- Baby screeming = 90 db

- Rock concert = 110 db
- Threshold of pain = 120 db.

The definition of the decibel in terms of logarithms masks the fact that the range of energies that the human person can hear is tremendous; it is 10 to the power of 12. The sense of sight also has this property – we can see a candle 100 yards away, and we can stare at the sun very briefly.

c) A physical wave of a string tied at both ends.

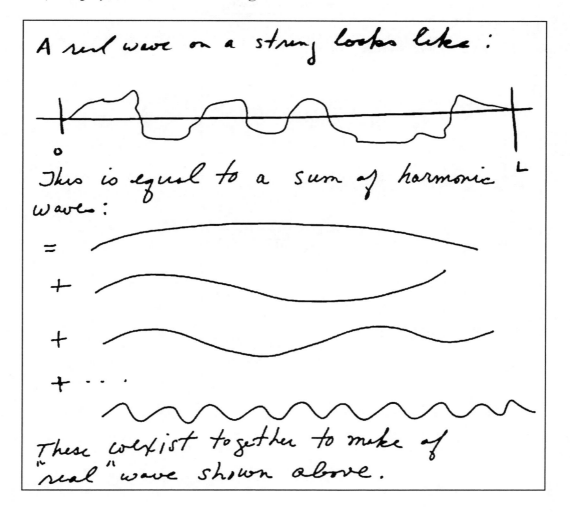

>   restart;y:=sin(Pi*x);y1:=sin(2*Pi*x);y2:=sin(3*Pi*x);   y3:=sin(4*Pi*x);
y4:=sin(5*Pi*x);

$$y := \sin(\pi\, x)$$
$$y1 := \sin(2\,\pi\, x)$$
$$y2 := \sin(3\,\pi\, x)$$
$$y3 := \sin(4\,\pi\, x)$$
$$y4 := \sin(5\,\pi\, x)$$

> plot({y,y1,y2,y3,y4},x=0..1);

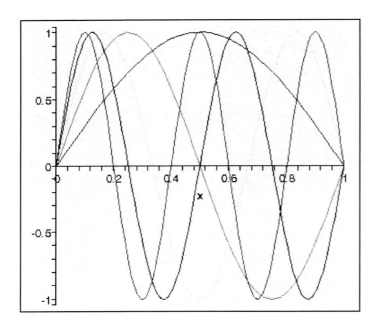

> yr:=-0.5*y+0.5*y1+0.5*y2+0.16*y3+0.3*y4;plot(yr,x=0..1);

$$yr := -0.5 \sin(\pi x) + 0.5 \sin(2 \pi x) + 0.5 \sin(3 \pi x) + 0.16 \sin(4 \pi x) + 0.3 \sin(5 \pi x)$$

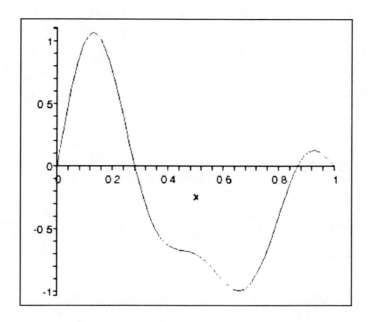

>

2.   The Doppler shift

A sound wave is a pressure wave moving in a medium such as air, and the sketch below can depict it:

high
Pressure
$hp \quad \lambda_0 \quad hp \quad hp \quad hp$

$v = 343 \, m/s$

$f = frequency = v/\lambda_0$

In this situation both the source of sound and the receiver are at rest.

This picture represents the case when the source of sound and the receiver of sound are not moving relative to the medium. When either source or receiver moves, the wave changes, and this change in the wave can be used to calculate the speeds of the source and the receiver.

The Doppler shift can be used to measure the speed of a moving horn. We will need to identify the source of sound (S) and the receiver of sound (R). The motion of either affects the frequency of the sound heard by R. We will consider the two separate cases where first S moves and R is stationary, and the second where S is stationary and R moves.

a) S moves with a speed v and R is at rest.

The wavelength in front of the moving source (horn) are crunched together, and the wavelengths behind are stretched apart.

λ_F = wavelength in front
v = speed of sound (343 m/s)
f_0 = frequency of sound from the horn

The receiver R (person in front hearing the horn) hears a frequency

$$f = \frac{v}{\lambda_F}$$

$$\lambda_F = \lambda_0\left(1 - \frac{v_S}{v}\right), \quad \lambda_0 = \frac{v}{f_0}$$

$$- = \frac{v}{\lambda_0(1 - v_S/v)} = f_0 \frac{1}{1 - v_S/v}$$

b) S is stationary and R moves toward the source with a speed v_R:

f_0 = frequency of horn ; λ_0 = wavelength

v = velocity of sound

v_R = velocity of R toward the stationary horn.

The receiver R hears a frequency f

$$f = \frac{\text{velocity of sound relative to R}}{\lambda_0}$$

$$= \frac{v + v_R}{\lambda_0} = \frac{v}{\lambda_0}\left(1 + \frac{v_R}{v}\right)$$

$$= f_0\left(1 + v_R/v\right)$$

c) The general case.

f = frequency heard by receiver (R)

f_0 = frequency of horn (S)

v = speed of sound = 343 m/s

v_s = velocity of S

v_R = velocity of R

$$f = f_0\left(\frac{1 \pm \frac{v_R}{v}}{1 \pm \frac{v_s}{v}}\right)$$

$\leftarrow$ R
$+$ toward
$-$ away

$\leftarrow$ $+$ S moving away

$-$ S moving toward

d) Example.

The whistle on a train emits a sound with a frequency 528 Hz. The train moves with a speed of 100 km/hr in the x direction toward a receiver at rest.

- What is the frequency heard by the receiver?

$$f_o = 528 \, hz$$

$$f = f_o \left(\frac{1}{1 - v_s/v} \right)$$

$$v_s = 100 \, \frac{km}{hr} \, \frac{1 \, hr}{3600 \, s} \, \frac{10^3 \, m}{1 \, km} = 27.8 \, m/s$$

$$f = 528 \, Hz \left(\frac{1}{1 - \frac{27.8}{343}} \right)$$

$$= 528 \, Hz \, \frac{1}{1 - 0.081} = \boxed{574 \, Hz}$$

- Suppose that the train is at the station still sounding its whistle and the R is a person in a car moving away from the train with a speed of 100 km/hr. What frequency does the person hear?

$$f = f_o \left(1 - \frac{v_R}{v} \right)$$

$$= 528 \, Hz \left(1 - \frac{27.8}{343} \right)$$

$$= 528 \, Hz \, (1 - 0.081) = \boxed{485 \, Hz}$$

- The train starts up and moves toward the speeding car with a speed of 100 km/s and sounds its whistle. What is the frequency of sound is heard by the driver of the car?

$$f = f_o \left(\frac{1 - v_R/v}{1 - v_L/v} \right) \quad \leftarrow R \text{ speed away}$$
$$\leftarrow S \text{ speed } R \text{ in front}$$

$$= 528 Hz \left(\frac{1 - \frac{27.8}{343}}{1 - 27.8/343} \right)$$

$$= 528 \, Hz$$

3. **The phenomenon of beats with the Doppler effect.**

a) Beats.

Two sounds of frequencies f_1 and f_2 in the same space will interfere with each other to product an embedded wave with a pulse frequency of $|f_1 - f_2|$. The embedded beat sound does not determine which frequency is larger.

b) Computer illustration.

Consider two tuning forks with frequencies 400 and 402 Hz. Sounding together in the same space. The following Maple program illustrates the result:

>restart;y1:=sin(2*Pi*x/343.0*400);y2:=sin(2*Pi*x/343.0*402);y:=y1+y2;

$$y1 := \sin(2.332361516\,\pi\,x)$$

$$y2 := \sin(2.344023324\,\pi\,x)$$

$$y := \sin(2.332361516\,\pi\,x) + \sin(2.344023324\,\pi\,x)$$

> plot({y1,y2},x=0..2);

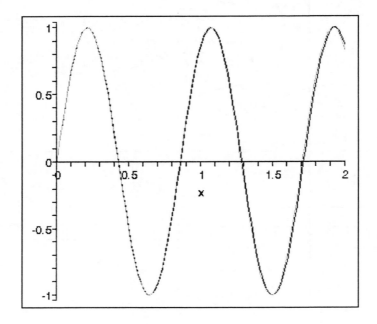

>
ybeat:=cos(2*Pi*x/342*2);plot(ybeat,x=0..500);plot({ybeat,y1+y2},x=0..500
);

$$ybeat := \cos\left(\frac{2}{171}\,\pi\,x\right)$$

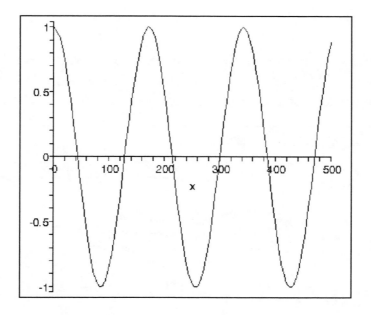

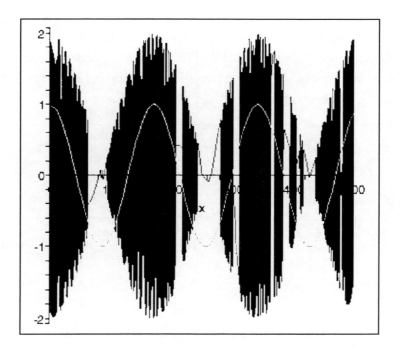

>

c) Example 1.

Two speakers sound in the same space with the wavelength of the
first equal to 80.1 cm and 79.71 cm for the second. What is the beat
pulse frequency of the resulting beats?

The frequencies are
$$f_1 = \frac{v}{\lambda_1} = \frac{343 m/s}{80.1 \times 10^{-2} m} = 428 \text{ Hz},$$
$$f_2 = \frac{v}{\lambda_2} = \frac{343 m/s}{79.71 \times 10^{-2} m} = 430 \text{ Hz}$$
$$\Rightarrow \text{Pulse frequency} = |f_1 - f_2| = 2 \text{ Hz}$$

d) Example 2.

Two tuning forks produce a beat pulse frequency of 4 Hz, and the
frequency of one of them is 330 Hz. When a piece of gum is stuck to
the unknown fork, the pulse frequency becomes 6 Hz. What is the
frequency of the unknown tuning for

Without the gum, the frequency of the fork
can have one of the two values
$$f_2 = 330 \pm 4 = \underline{334 \text{ Hz}} \text{ or } \underline{226 \text{ Hz}}$$
With the gum, the frequency of the unknown
fork is f_2', and

f_2'	f_2	f_1	f_2	f_2'
224	226	330 Hz	334	336

But placing gum on a tuning fork will
lower its frequency, so the only possibility is
$$\boxed{f_2 = 226 \text{ Hz}}$$

e) Example 3.

Speed measurement using the Doppler shift and the beat phenomenon. The horn on a police car sounds at a frequency f = 150 Hz. The police car is parked at the side of the road. A car races toward the police car with an unknown speed of v_{car}. The sound from the is heard by the car as a doppler-shifted frequency f', and it bounces back to the police as if form a horn of frequency f'. This returning sound reaches the police car as another Doppler-shifted sound wave with a frequency f''. Inside the police car the original sound of the horn of frequency f and the returning sound of frequency f'' produce a beat pulse frequency of 20 beats/second. What is v_{car}?

Police horn

$f = 150 \, Hz$

$f'' =$ frequency received

$|f - f''| = 20 \, beats/sec$

reflected sound f'

Using the Doppler equations:

$$f' = 150 \, Hz \left(1 + \frac{v_{car}}{v} \right)$$

$$f'' = f' \frac{1}{(1 - v_{car}/v)}$$

$$= 150 \, Hz \left(\frac{1 + v_{car}/v}{1 - v_{car}/v} \right)$$

Apply my the beat effect gives

$$f'' - f = 20 \, Hz = 150 \left(\frac{1 + v_{car}/v}{1 - v_{car}/v} \right) - 150$$

So

$$\frac{20 + 150}{150} = \frac{1 + v_{car}/v}{1 - v_{car}/v} = \frac{170}{150} = 1.133$$

$$1 + \frac{v_{car}}{343} = 1.133\left(1 - \frac{v_{car}}{343}\right)$$

$$\frac{v_{car}}{343}(1 + 1.133) = (1.133 - 1)$$

$$v_{car} = \frac{0.133}{2.133} \cdot 343\,m/s = 21.4\frac{m}{s}$$

$$v_{car} = 21.4\,m/s\left(\frac{2.237\,mph}{1\,m/s}\right) = \boxed{47.9\ mph}$$

CHAPTER 10

Optics

This subject actually extends back to Newton who was the first scientist to separate visible light into its colors. Sound provides are sense of hearing with information about our environment and about reality. Light provides independent information through the sense of sight. Let's compare sound and light:

<u>Sound</u>

1. Pressure wave in a medium

2. $v = 343 \, m/s$ (air)

3. Speed of sound depends on speed of the receiver

4. $f\lambda = v$

5. Human reception
$20 \, Hz \rightarrow 20,000 \, Hz$
$17.1 \, m \rightarrow 1.72 \, cm$

<u>Light</u>

1. Electromagnetic wave in space (medium not needed)

2. $v = c = 3 \times 10^8 \, m/s$

3. Speed of light doesn't depend on the speed of the receiver

4. $f\lambda = c$

5. Human reception
Red $\longrightarrow$ Violet
$4.4 \times 10^{14} \, Hz \rightarrow 8.1 \times 10^{14} \, Hz$
$7 \times 10^{-7} \, m \longrightarrow 3.75 \times 10^{-7} \, m$
$(700 \, nm)$ $(375 \, nm)$

We see that the frequencies of light that are visible to us are quite limited.

1.	Image Formation and the pinhole camera

a) The nature of light.

Light is an electromagnetic wave that moves in space without the need for a medium with the speed $c = 3 \times 10^8$ m/s. The speed of light does not depend on the motion of the receiver as in the case of sound waves.

The frequencies of light that are visible to us are quite limited. Expressed in terms of wavelengths some examples are:

Near ultraviolet = 361 nm in air
Blue = 434 nm
Blue-Green = 486 nm
Yellow = 589 nm
Orange = 656 nm
Red = 768 nm
Infrared (heat radiation) = 1200 nm, where 1 nm = 10^{-9} m.

The primary colors are red, green and blue, and they can be combined to produce other colors. For example red and green light produces the sensation of yellow to the brain; red and blue produces purple; all three produce the sensation of white light. White light is, in fact, the effect in the brain of the reception of all visible frequencies equally weighted – there is no single wavelength of white light.

Mixing paints is not the same as mixing colored light – it is a subtractive rather than an additive process. Mixing all the colors of paint will produce a dark brown color.

b) Light rays and image formation.

Although light is a wave, when the wavelength of the light (500 nm) is small compared to the objects that the light encounters (mirrors, lenses and eyes), its effect can be determined by picturing the light as moving in straight lines or rays.

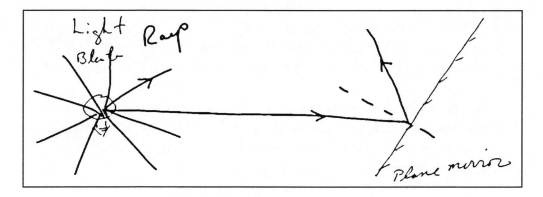

In describing image formation, we will work with rays of light as they encounter holes, mirrors, glass plates, lenses and the human eye. Image formation means that we trace by the use of light rays, the position of the light from a point source toward a destination point such as a screen or a film plane.

c) The pinhole camera.

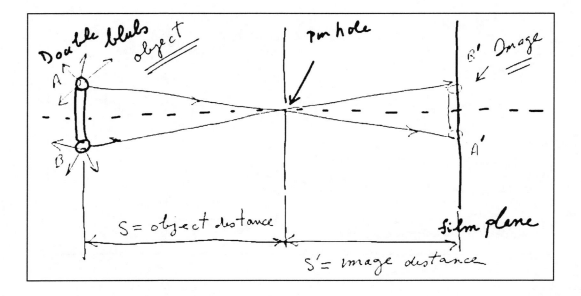

Points A and B are objects – the two light bulbs. Points A' and B' are the respective image points of A and B.
Characterization of the image:

- The image is real; it actually falls on the film plane and the developed picture will show the double bulb.
- The image is inverted – the bulbs are upside down.
- If s = s', the object and the image are the same size; if s > s', the object is larger than the image or the image is reduced; if s < s', the image is larger than the object or the image is magnified.

The pin-hole camera has the advantage that everything is in focus when the object is any distance from the hole. Its disadvantage is that the light passing through the hole is essentially one ray or very dim. One needs an extraordinarily bright object to form a strong image.

2.	Images formed by plane mirrors.

a) The law of reflection.

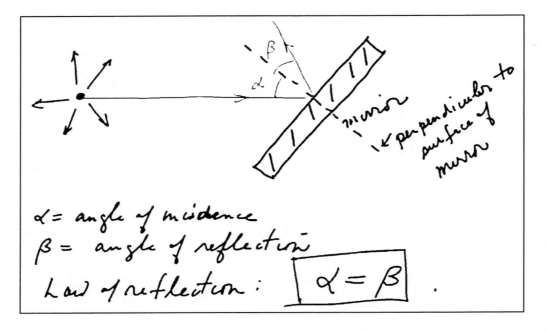

α = angle of incidence
β = angle of reflection
Law of reflection : $\boxed{\alpha = \beta}$.

b) Image of a candle formed by a plane mirror.

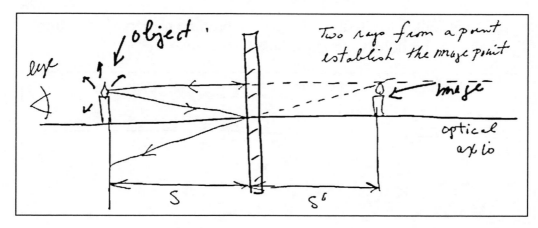

Characterization the image:

- The image is **virtual;** it appears to be inside the mirror. The two rays of reflected light from the image of the flame actually diverge and require and eye to bring them to focus.
- The image is **upright**.
- The image is **reversed** (right and left are reversed).
- Using the geometry shown with the angle of incidence equal to the angle of reflection, one can show that s = s'. This means that the size of the image is the same as the size of the object.

c) The image formed by two mirrors at right angles.

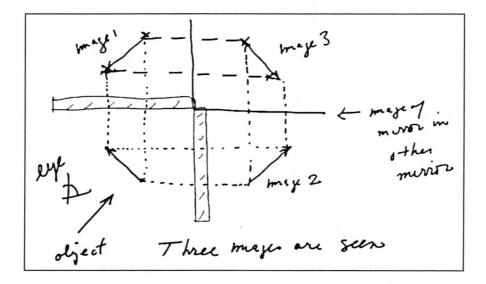

d) Example 1

A 4 cm ball is located 50 cm from a pinhole camera. If the film is 10 cm from the hole, what is the size of the image?

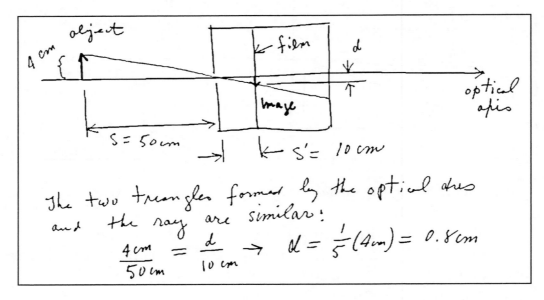

The two triangles formed by the optical axis and the ray are similar:

$$\frac{4\,cm}{50\,cm} = \frac{d}{10\,cm} \rightarrow d = \frac{1}{5}(4cm) = 0.8\,cm$$

e) Example 2.

The position of an object and an observer (eye) are placed in front of a plane mirror 30 cm apart and 2m from the mirror. What is the distance of the observer from the image?

$$D = \sqrt{4m^2 + (.3m)^2} = 4.01\,m$$

3. The formation of images by concave spherical mirrors.

a) The concave spherical mirror.

When the object is outside the center of the mirror.

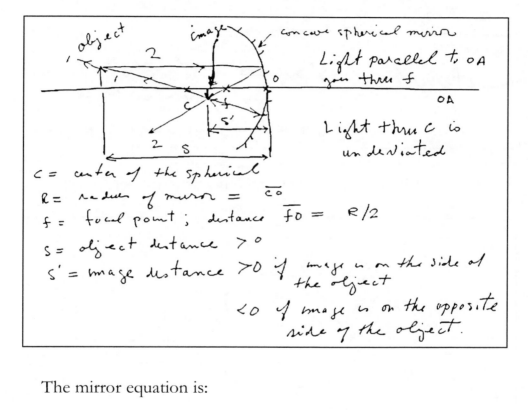

The mirror equation is:

$$1/S + 1/S' = 1/f, \; f = R/2.$$

b) Example 1.

A spherical mirror has a radius R = 1m and an object is placed 1.5 m from the mirror (measured from the optical axis). Find and characterize the image.

$$R = 1m, \quad S = 1.5m, \quad f = R/2 = 0.5m$$

$$\frac{1}{s} + \frac{1}{s'} = \frac{1}{f} \Rightarrow \frac{1}{1.5m} + \frac{1}{s'} = \frac{1}{.5m}$$

$$\Rightarrow \frac{1}{s'} = 2 - \frac{1}{1.5} = 1.333 \, m^{-1} \Rightarrow s' = 0.75m$$

$$m = magnification = -\frac{s'}{s} = -\frac{0.75}{1.5} = -0.5$$

definition

characterization: $\quad s' > 0 \Rightarrow$ real image

$m < 0 \Rightarrow$ inverted image

$|m| < 1 \Rightarrow$ reduced image

If the object is between f and C, the ray traces are as follows:

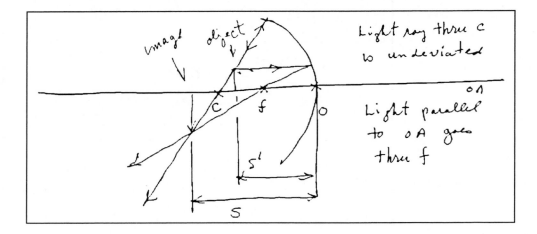

The mirror equation is the same as in case a).

c) Example 2.

A concave mirror of radius 1 m has an object placed 0.75 m from the mirror. Find and characterize the image.

$$R = 1m \quad , \quad f = R/2 = 0.5m \quad , \quad S = 0.75m$$

$$\frac{1}{s} + \frac{1}{s'} = \frac{1}{f} \Rightarrow \frac{1}{.75m} + \frac{1}{s'} = \frac{1}{.5m} \Rightarrow$$

$$\frac{1}{s'} = \frac{1}{.5} - \frac{1}{.75} = 0.6667 m^{-1} \Rightarrow \boxed{s' = 1.5m}$$

$$m = -\frac{s'}{s} = -\frac{1.5}{.75} = -2.0$$

$$s' > 0 \Rightarrow \text{real image}$$

$$m < 0 \Rightarrow \text{inverted}$$

$$|m| > 1 \Rightarrow \text{enlarge or magnified}$$

If the Object is between f and the mirror surface, the ray tracing becomes:

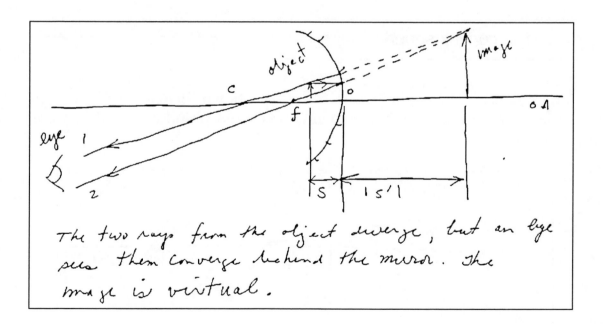

The two rays from the object diverge, but an eye sees them converge behind the mirror. The image is virtual.

d) Example 3.

A concave mirror of radius 1m has an object placed at 0.4 m. from the mirror's surface. Find and characterize the image.

$$R = 1 \, m, \quad f = R/2 = 0.5m, \quad S = 0.4m$$

$$\frac{1}{s} + \frac{1}{s'} = \frac{1}{f} \rightarrow \frac{1}{0.4m} + \frac{1}{s'} = \frac{1}{.5m} \rightarrow \frac{1}{s'} = \frac{1}{.5} - \frac{1}{.4}$$

$$= -0.5 \, m^{-1}$$

$$\rightarrow \boxed{s' = -2m}$$

$$s' < 0 \rightarrow \text{virtual image}$$

$$m = -s'/s = -(-2)/.4 = +5$$

$$m > 0 \rightarrow \text{upright}$$

$$|m| > 1 \rightarrow \text{magnified.}$$

---

4.   The convex spherical mirror.

This spherical mirror bulges outward as shown below, and the sign convention for the analysis is that the radius and primary focal distance is negative:

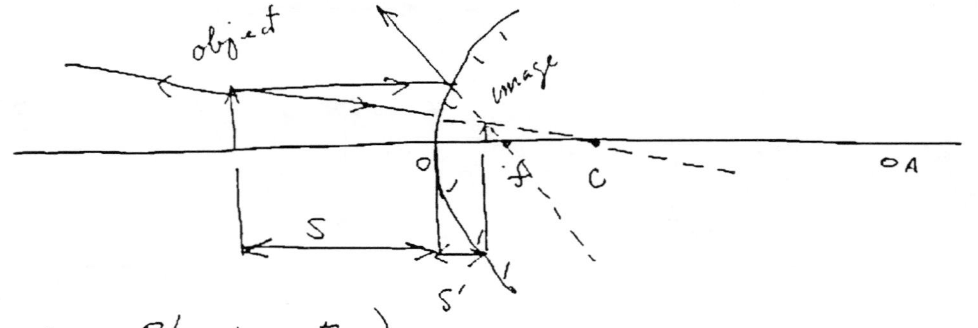

$$f = -R/2 \ (\text{negative})$$

Images formed will always be virtual

As an example, consider a concave spherical mirror has a radius of 1 m and a focal length of f = -R/2 = −0.5 m. An object is placed 1 m from the surface. Find the location of the image and characterize it.

$$f = -0.5m, \quad S = 1.5m,$$

$$\frac{1}{s} + \frac{1}{s'} = \frac{1}{f} \rightarrow \frac{1}{1.5m} + \frac{1}{s'} = \frac{1}{-.5m} \rightarrow \frac{1}{s'} = -2 - 0.667$$

$$\frac{1}{s'} = -2.667 \rightarrow \boxed{s' = -0.375m}$$

$$m = -s'/s = -\frac{(-.375)}{1.5} = 0.25$$

$$m > 0 \Rightarrow upright$$

$$|m| < 1 \Rightarrow reduced$$

$$s' < 0 \Rightarrow virtual$$

---

5.   The refraction of light and the index of refraction.

a) The index of refraction.

The speed of light in a vacuum is c = 3×10^8 m/s. However, in a medium such as glass, the average speed through the medium can reduce because the light is bouncing between atoms. The speed of light in a medium is

$$v_n = c/n, \quad n = \text{index of refraction of the medium.}$$

Examples of the index of refraction are:

n(air) = 1.0,
n(water) = 1.33,
n(glass) = 1.5 (but varies with the type of glass),
n(diamond) = 2.4.

b) Application of the law of refraction.

A lens is an object made of a medium like glass that receivess light incident from another medium like air. So there is an air-glass interface, and this bends the light:

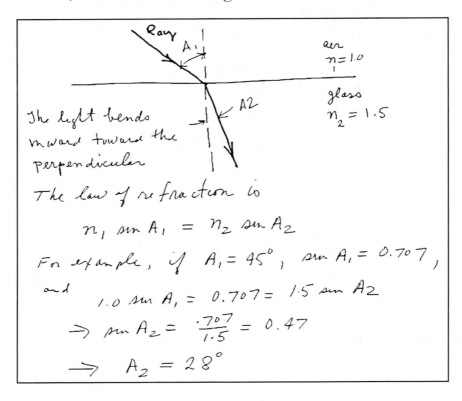

Ray

A₁

air
$n = 1.0$

A2

glass
$n_2 = 1.5$

The light bends inward toward the perpendicular

The law of refraction is

$$n_1 \sin A_1 = n_2 \sin A_2$$

For example, if $A_1 = 45°$, $\sin A_1 = 0.707$,

and

$$1.0 \sin A_1 = 0.707 = 1.5 \sin A_2$$

$$\Rightarrow \sin A_2 = \frac{.707}{1.5} = 0.47$$

$$\Rightarrow A_2 = 28°$$

c) Image formation by thin lenses.

A thin lens is so thin that its thickness, he distance between the two spherical surfaces is negligible in the lens equation. Such lenses come in four different shapes depicted as:

Converging   light →   ()   convex — convex

Converging
or diverging   →   ((convex — concave

→   ))   concave — convex

Diverging   →   )(concave — concave

d) The thin lens formulas.

$$1/s + 1/s' = 1/f,$$
$$m = -s'/s.$$

Here, s is the object distance, s' is the image distance and f is the focal length. The sign conventions are the same as for mirrors: s' > 0 means a real image; s' < 0 means a virtual image; f > 0 is a converging lens; f < 0 is a diverging lens.

e) Drawing of the formation of an image.

The critical element in the drawing is the optical axis (OA). It is a straight line through the center of the lens as shown. Rays of light are incident from the right, pass through the lends, and the light projects back into the air at the left.

f) Example.

A thin lens made of glass has a focal length of 22 cm, and an object is placed 32 cm to the left of the lens. Find and characterize the image.

$$\frac{1}{s} + \frac{1}{s'} = \frac{1}{f} \rightarrow \frac{1}{32cm} + \frac{1}{s'} = \frac{1}{22cm}$$

$$\frac{1}{s'} = \frac{1}{22} - \frac{1}{32} = 0.01420 \rightarrow s' = 70.4cm$$

$$m = -s'/s = -70.4/32 = -2.2$$

Characterize :   s' > 0   real

                 . m < 0   inverted

                 |m| > 1   magnified

g) Image formed by a diverging lens.

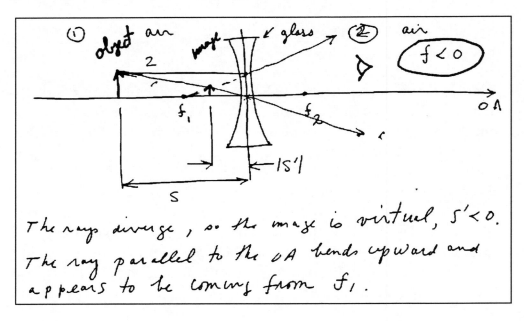

The rays diverge, so the image is virtual, $s' < 0$. The ray parallel to the OA bends upward and appears to be coming from f_1.

h) Example

A diverging lens has a focal length of −22 cm. An object is placed to the right of the lens at s = 50 cm. Find and characterize the image.

$$S = 50 \text{ cm}, \quad f = -22 \text{ cm}$$

$$\frac{1}{s} + \frac{1}{s'} = \frac{1}{f} \Rightarrow \frac{1}{50 \text{ cm}} + \frac{1}{s'} = \frac{1}{-22 \text{ cm}}$$

$$\frac{1}{s'} = \frac{1}{-22} - \frac{1}{50} = -0.06545$$

$$s' = -15.3 \text{ cm}$$

$$m = -s'/s = -\frac{(-15.3)}{50} = +0.306$$

characterize → $\quad s' < 0 \rightarrow$ virtual

$\quad\quad\quad\quad\quad\quad\quad m > 0 \rightarrow$ upright

$\quad\quad\quad\quad\quad\quad\quad |m| < 1 \rightarrow$ reduced

i)   Image formed by a combination of two lenses.

A converging and diverging lens are used in combination to form an image. Many optical instruments, including the human eye, are so configured. We will place the lenses close together so that their separation distance can be neglected.

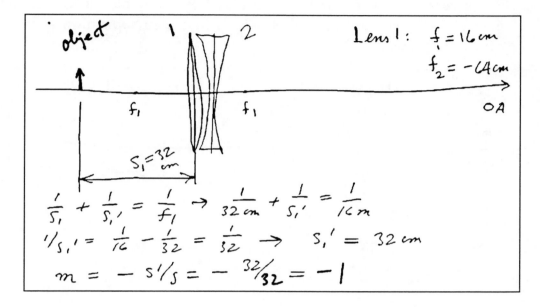

We now take the image formed by the first lens and regard it as the object for the diverging second lens. Note that $s_2 = -32$ cm.

$$Lens\ 2 \qquad f_2 = -64cm, \quad S_2 = -32\ cm$$

$$\frac{1}{S_2} + \frac{1}{S_2'} = \frac{1}{f_2} \rightarrow \frac{1}{-32cm} + \frac{1}{S_2'} = \frac{1}{-64cm}$$

$$\frac{1}{S_2'} = -\frac{1}{64} + \frac{1}{32} = \frac{1}{64} \rightarrow S_2' = 64\ cm$$

$$m_2 = -S_2'/S_2 = -\frac{(64)}{-32} = 2$$

$$m = m_1 m_2 = (-1)(2) = -2$$

6.   Compound Lenses. The Human Eye

a) Image formation by two thin lenses close together.

A converging and diverging lens are used in combination to form an image. The lenses are close together so that their separation distance can be neglected.

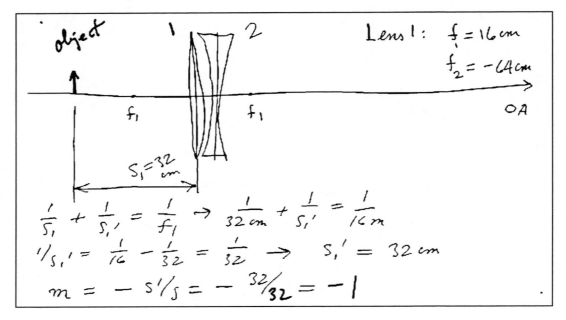

We now take the image formed by the first lens and regard it as the object for the diverging second lens. Note that $s_2 = -32$ cm.

b) Short-cut.

For two thin lenses close together of focal length f_1 and f_2, the combination lens has a focal length f given by

$$1/f = 1/f_1 + 1/f_2.$$

For the above example, $f_1 = 16$ cm and $f_2 = -64$ cm. The combination close together has a focal length
$$\frac{1}{f} = \frac{1}{16\,cm} + \frac{1}{-64\,cm} = \frac{4}{64} - \frac{1}{64} = \frac{3}{64}$$
$$\rightarrow f = \frac{64}{3} = 21.33\ cm.$$
if $S = 32$ cm,
$$\frac{1}{s} + \frac{1}{s'} = \frac{1}{21.33} = \frac{3}{64}$$
$$\frac{1}{s'} = \frac{3}{64} - \frac{1}{32} = \frac{3}{64} - \frac{2}{64} = \frac{1}{64}$$
$$\rightarrow s' = 64\ cm$$
$$m = -s'/s = -(64/32) = -2$$
This agrees with the longer calculation.

c) The Diopter.

The form of the equation for lens combinations suggests that the inverse of the focal length of a lens has a special importance. The Diopter is defined as

Diopter, D = 1/f, f = focal length of a lens in meters.

With this definition, the Diopter of a lens combination is given by

$$D(\text{combination}) = D_1 + D_2.$$

As an example, consider two thin lenses have focal lengths of 20 cm and − 50 cm and are close together. What is the diopter and focal length in centimeters of the combination?

$$f_1 = 20 \text{ cm}, \quad f_2 = -50 \text{ cm}$$

$$D_1 = \frac{1}{.2 \text{ m}} = 5.0$$

$$D_2 = \frac{1}{-.5 \text{ m}} = -20$$

Thus,

$$D \text{ combination} = 5.0 - 2.0 = 3.0,$$

and

$$f_{comb} = \frac{1}{3} = 0.333 \text{ m} = 33.3 \text{ cm}.$$

d) The healthy human eye.

- Physical construction and far point.

   Light is incident on the eye from a source far away (far means much longer the size of eye). The light is brought to focus on the retina by the eye. The eye is actually a two-lens system − the cornia is fixed and the "lens" is variable. The variable lens is squeezed by muscles so that its thickness varies and hence its focal length varies. The distance from the iris, like the diaphragm of a camera, is 1.7 cm.

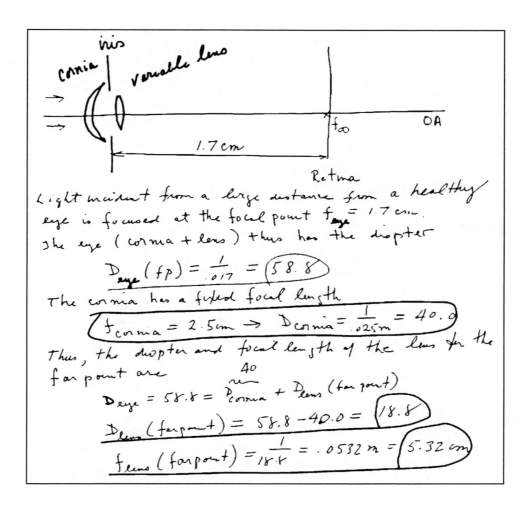

The following appears within the boxed figure area:

Light incident from a large distance from a healthy eye is focused at the focal point $f_{eye} = 1.7$ cm. The eye (cornea + lens) thus has the diopter

$$D_{eye}(fp) = \frac{1}{.017} = \boxed{58.8}$$

The cornia has a fixed focal length

$$\boxed{f_{cornia} = 2.5 cm \Rightarrow D_{cornia} = \frac{1}{.025 m} = 40.0}$$

Thus, the diopter and focal length of the lens for the far point are

$$D_{eye} = 58.8 = \overset{40}{P_{cornia}} + D_{lens}(far\ point)$$

$$\underline{D_{lens}(far\ point) = 58.8 - 40.0 = \boxed{18.8}}$$

$$\underline{f_{lens}(far\ point) = \frac{1}{18.8} = .0532\ m = \boxed{5.32\ cm}}$$

- The near point.

   A healthy eye can bring an object at 25 cm from the lens into focus on the retina. The diopter and focal length of the lens for the near point is:

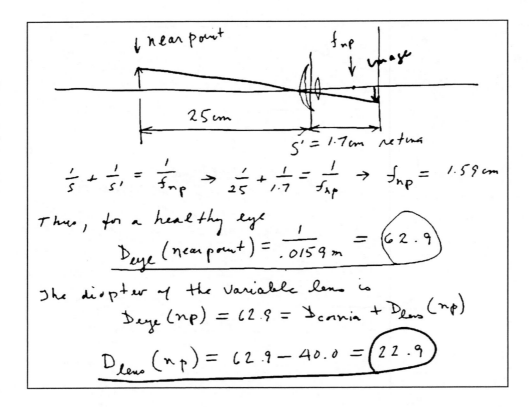

We then note that for a healthy eye, the variable lens changes its shape so the D_{lens} (far point at infinity) = 18.8, and D_{lens} (near point) = 22.9. The difference is 22.9 – 18.8 = 4 diopters.

e) Corrective lenses for imperfect eyes.

The myopic eye. A "near sighted" person cannot see far object but can focus objects nearer the eye than a normal eye. The image of far-away objects gets focus in front of the retina. A diverging corrective lens is needed.

Example. a person has a far point of 22 cm and a near point of 13 cm. What corrective lens will allow this person to see objects at infinity?

The focal length of the eye:
$$\frac{1}{s} + \frac{1}{s'} = \frac{1}{f_{eye}} \rightarrow \frac{1}{22 cm} + \frac{1}{1.7 cm} = \frac{1}{f_{eye}} \rightarrow f_{eye} = 1.58 cm$$

$$D_{eye} = \frac{1}{.0158 m} = 63.3 \text{ diopter}$$

A corrective lens is need to make this eye behave healthy; i.e. $D_{eye}(fp) = 58.8 = D_{eye}(corrected)$

$$D_{eye}(corrected) = 58.8 = D_{eye} + D_{correction}$$
$$= 63.3 + D_{correction}$$

$\rightarrow D_{correction} = 58.8 - 63.3 = \boxed{-4.5}$

$f_{correction} = \frac{-1}{4.5} = -.222 m = \boxed{-22.2 cm}$

f) The hyperopic eye. Some eyes can see objects far away but are unable to bring to focus close objects. The variable lens is unable to bend light enough to bring such images to focus on the retina – the image is in back of the retina.

To illustrate, consider a person with a near point of 70 cm. What corrective lens is needed to allow reading at 25 cm?

Focal length of the eye for its near point:

$$\frac{1}{70 cm} + \frac{1}{1.7 cm} = \frac{1}{f_{eye}} \rightarrow f_{eye} = 1.66 cm$$

$$D_{eye} = \frac{1}{.0166} = 60.25 \text{ diopter}$$

We need a corrective lens that makes this eye appear healthy for an object at 25 cm; i.e. $D_{eye}(corrected) = 62.8.$

$$D_{eye}(corrected) = 62.8 = D_{eye} + D_{correction}$$
$$= 60.25 + D_{correction}$$

$\rightarrow D_{correction} = 62.8 - 60.25 = \boxed{2.6}$

$f_{correction} = \frac{1}{2.6} = .385 = \boxed{38.5 cm}$

7.	Optical Instruments

a) Corrective lenses.

Optical instruments all have the eye as part of the design. They all have eye pieces that are used with other lenses to do the required task. So let us again return to the mechanics of the eye.

We have already seen that a healthy eye can focus an object placed at the near point (25 cm) and bring it to focus on the retina. The diopter of the healthy eye for the near point is 62.8. The diopter of the eye for the far point is 58.8. Thus a normal eye has a variable lens whose shape for the far point is 22.8, and its shape for the near point is 18.8. The difference between these extremes is in diopter is 4. The muscles controlling the eye are most relaxed for the far point.

- The myoptic eye. Example. a person has a far point of 22 cm and a near point of 13 cm. What corrective lens will allow this person to see objects at infinity? This example done in the last lecture led to a corrective lens of diopter −4.5. A single diverging lens does the trick.

- The hyperopic eye. Some eyes can see objects far away but are unable to bring to focus close objects. The variable lens is unable to bend light enough to bring such images to focus on the retina – the image is in back of the retina.

A person has a near point of 70 cm. What corrective lens is needed to allow reading at 30 cm?

The focal length of a healty eye for $s = 70\,cm$ is

$$\frac{1}{s} + \frac{1}{s_1} = \frac{1}{f_{eye}} \rightarrow \frac{1}{30} + \frac{1}{1.7} = \frac{1}{f_{eye}} \rightarrow f_{eye} = 1.609\,cm$$

$$\rightarrow \underline{D_{eye} = \frac{1}{.01609} = 62.16\ diopter}$$

The far-sighted eye sees no closer than 70 cm, so

$$\frac{1}{70} + \frac{1}{1.7} = \frac{1}{f_{eye}} \rightarrow f_{eye}\ (far\text{-}sighted) = 1.660\,cm$$

$$\rightarrow \underline{D_{eye}\ (far\ sighted) = \frac{1}{.0166} = 60.24\ diopter}$$

The required correction is

$$D_{eye} = D_{eye}\ (far\ sighted) + D_{correction}$$

$$\rightarrow D_{correction} = 62.16 - 60.24 = \boxed{1.9\ diopter}$$

b) The magnifying glass or eyepiece.

We first note that all optical instruments assume the presence of a normal eye. They all produce an image to the eye that is virtual and essentially a far-point object so that the eye is most relaxed. We will calculate the angular magnification of an object by comparing how the eye sees the object under the magnifier to how the eye sees an object without the magnifier at its near point.

- The largest image of an object studied by the eye without a magnifier:

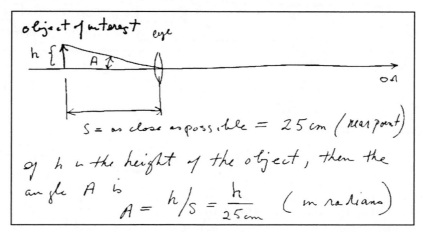

$$A = h/s = \frac{h}{25 cm} \quad (in\ radians)$$

- The angle of sight with a magnifying glass.

The angle A' is
$$A' = |h'/s'|$$
where $h' = h m = -h s'/s$ as $m = -s'/s$.
So,
$$A' = \left| -\frac{h s'}{s s'} \right|$$

We recall that the angle of sight for view the object as large as possible without a magnifier is A = h/25 cm, so

$$A' = \left| -\frac{s'\,h}{s\,s'} \right| = \left| \frac{-s'\,(A\,25cm)}{s\,s'} \right|$$

$$= \frac{25\,cm}{s}\,A = \frac{25\,cm}{f}\,A$$

The angular magnification is

$$\boxed{m_A = 25\,cm/f} \quad , \quad f = \text{focal length of magnifier}$$

This result holds for all eyepieces, which are essentially magnifying glasses. For example, an eyepiece of focal length f = 10 cm has an angular magnification of

$$m_A = 25\ cm/\ 10\ cm = 2.5.$$

This means that the object under study appears 2.5 times larger to the eye than it would if placed as the near point of the eye without an eyepiece.

c)   The microscope. The microscope takes a small object and places the image of that object at the focal point of the eyepiece. The angular magnification of the object therefore consists of the magnification due to an objective lens times the magnification of the eyepiece.

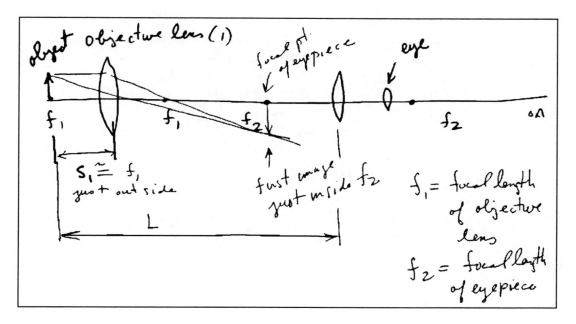

The geometry of the microscope determines the total angular magnification of the original object, and the result is

$$M_A = L\, 25\ \text{cm}/(f_1\, f_2).\ \text{(microscope)}.$$

To illustrate, consider a microscope has a length L = 15 cm, an objective whose focal length is f_1 = 5 mm and an eyepiece whose focal length is f_2 = 2 cm. What is its magnification?

$$M_A = \frac{L(25\,cm)}{f_1\,f_2} = \frac{15\,cm\,(25\,cm)}{(.5\,cm)(2\,cm)} = 375$$

The microscope magnifies the original object 375 times the size it would appear at the near point without an instrument.

d) The telescope.

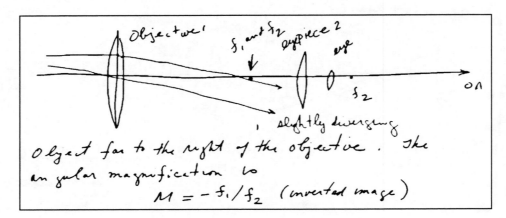

Object far to the right of the objective. The angular magnification is

$$M = -f_1/f_2 \quad (\text{inverted image})$$

CHAPTER 11

The Wave Nature of Light

---

1. Wave interference in terms of distance traveled.

---

a) Two waves displaced in space by one-half wavelength.

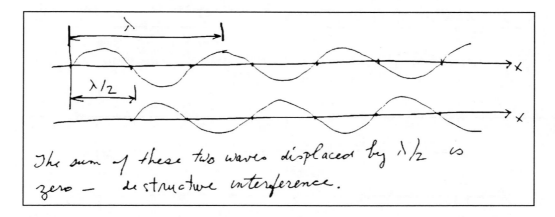

The sum of these two waves displaced by λ/2 is zero — destructive interference.

b) Two waves displaced by one wavelength.

In this case the two wave line up and they add to together to produce constructive interference.

---

2. Proof that light is a wave.
(demo using lasers and theory).

Light of wavelength λ is incident on a plate that has two parallel slits cut into it. The slits are a distance d apart. After the light emerges from the slits, it falls on a screen and patterns of light and dark fringes are observed on the screen.

a) Wave construction.

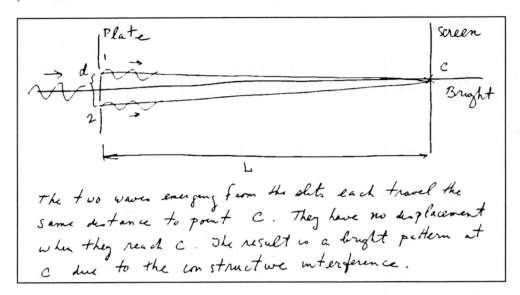

The two waves emerging from the slits each travel the same distance to point C. They have no displacement when they reach C. The result is a bright pattern at C due to the constructive interference.

Further down from the central bright pattern, one finds a region of darkness. The wave construction follows:

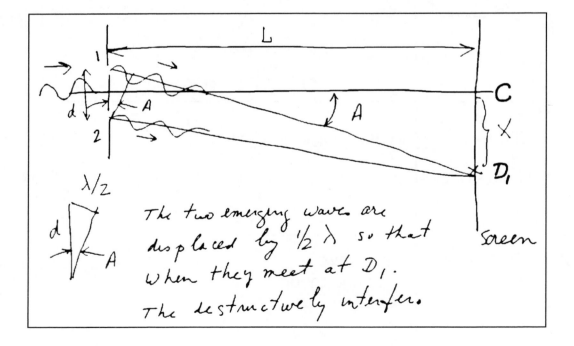

The two emerging waves are displaced by ½ λ so that when they meet at D_1. The destructively interfer.

b) The mathematical relationship between the parameters above:

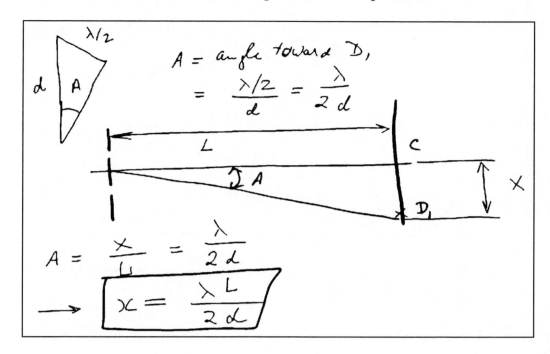

Thus, the distance on the screen from the central bright pattern to the first dark region is x = λ L/ (2d). The distance to the second bright pattern is 2x; the distance to the second dark region is 3x; the distance to the third bright patter is 4x, and so on. A pattern of bright and dark fringes is seen on the screen.

Since we have observed this for laser light, light is indeed a wave phenomenon.

- Example. Green light of wavelength 600 nm is incident on a double slit system where the slits are separated by d = 0.2 mm.

  (1) Find the angle to the first dark fringe.
  (2) If the distance form the slit plate to the screen is L = 5 m, what is the distance from the center bright fringe to the first dark fringe.
  (3) What is the distance to the from the center fringe pattern to the 5th bright fringe?

$$(1) \quad A = \frac{\lambda}{2d} = \frac{600 \times 10^{-9}m}{2(2 \times 10^{-4}m)} = 0.0015 \text{ radian}$$

$$= 0.0015 \text{ rad} \frac{360°}{2\pi \text{ rad}} = 0.0859 \text{ degrees}$$

$$(2) \quad x = L\frac{\lambda}{2d} = LA = (5m)(.0015 \text{ radians})$$

$$= 75 \times 10^{-3} m = 75 mm$$

$$(3) \quad x(\text{to 5th bright fringe}) = 10 \times$$
$$\text{from center} \qquad = 7.5 cm$$

c) Fringe pattern formed by light incident normally on a thin film (like a soap bubble of a lens coating).

- Wave displacement (phase change) due to reflection and refraction.

If $n_1 < n_2$ (air to glass),

Wave 1 is incident

Wave 2 is reflected and displaced by $\frac{\lambda}{2}$

Wave 3 is refracted and not displaced,
but $\lambda' = \lambda(n_1/n_2) < \lambda$

If $n_1 > n_2$ (glass to air),

Wave 1 is incident

Wave 2 is reflected and not displaced

Wave 3 is refracted and not displaced,
but $\lambda' = \lambda(n_1/n_2) > \lambda$.

e) Wave interference when light is incident normally on a thin film (soap of index 1.33).

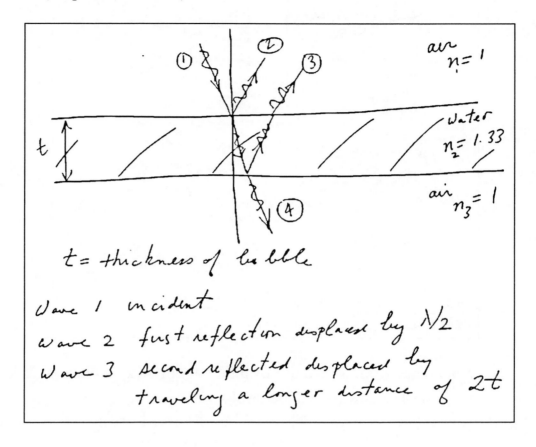

t = thickness of bubble

Wave 1 incident

Wave 2 first reflection displaced by $\lambda/2$

Wave 3 second reflected displaced by traveling a longer distance of $2t$

---

3.   Useful applications of light interference

a) Reflection cancellation or enhancement by light incident normally on a thin film (like a soap bubble of a lens coating).

• Wave displacement (phase change) and wavelength change due to reflection and refraction.

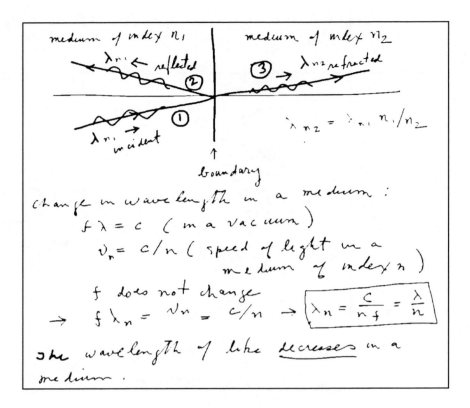

When light from a medium of index n_1 enters a medium of index n_2, the reflected wave will be displaced by $\lambda/2$ if $n_2 > n_1$.

The reflected wave will not be displaced if $n_2 < n_1$. The wavelengths in the two media are different according to the equation

$$\lambda_1/\lambda_2 = n_2/n_1.$$

The wavelength of light is a medium is not changed by reflection or refraction.

- The reflection of red light ($\lambda_1 = 700$ nm) from a soap bubble ($n_2 = 1.330$) in air ($n_1 = 1$) of thickness 263 nm.

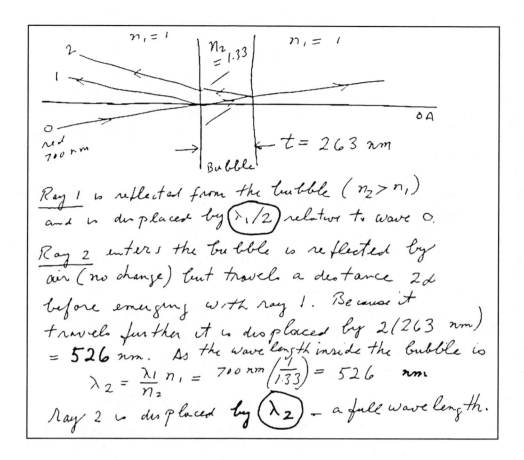

Ray 1 is reflected from the bubble ($n_2 > n_1$)
and is displaced by $\boxed{\lambda_1 / 2}$ relative to wave 0.

Ray 2 enters the bubble is reflected by
air (no change) but travels a distance $2d$
before emerging with ray 1. Because it
travels further it is displaced by 2(263 nm)
= 526 nm. As the wave length inside the bubble is
$$\lambda_2 = \frac{\lambda_1}{n_2} n_1 = 700\,nm \left(\frac{1}{1.33}\right) = 526 \quad nm$$
Ray 2 is displaced by $\boxed{\lambda_2}$ — a full wave length.

Thus, when ray 1 emerges, it is displaced by $\lambda/2$ due to reflection. When ray 2 emerges, it is displaced by λ due to traveling a longer distance. When we compare these two reflected rays, they are $\lambda - \lambda/2 = \lambda/2$ apart, and so they destructively interfere. There is no reflected wave.

If the soap bubble had one-half the thickness, ie 132 nm, the two reflected waves would constructively interfere, and there would be enhanced reflection of the red light.

Summary: reflection from a thin film of index higher than air:

$$t = \text{thickness of film} = \lambda_2/2 => \text{destructive}$$
$$= 3\,\lambda_2/2 => \text{destructive}$$
$$= 5\,\lambda_2/2 => \text{destructive};$$

$$t = \text{thickness of film} = \lambda_2/4 => \text{constructive}$$
$$= 3\,\lambda_2/4 => \text{constructive}$$
$$= 5\,\lambda_2/4 => \text{constructive.}$$

The same kind of result will occur for a thin film on glass (lens coating) if the index of the film is higher than the index of the glass.

b) The limit of resolution of an image formed by a lens due to light interference.

- Image of a point of light formed by a lens on a film plane.

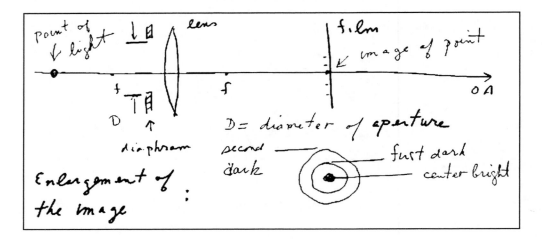

The pattern of fringes around the central maximum depends on the diameter of the aperture D - the smaller the aperture, the larger the fringe pattern of rings surrounding the central point.

- The limit of resolution of two points of light.

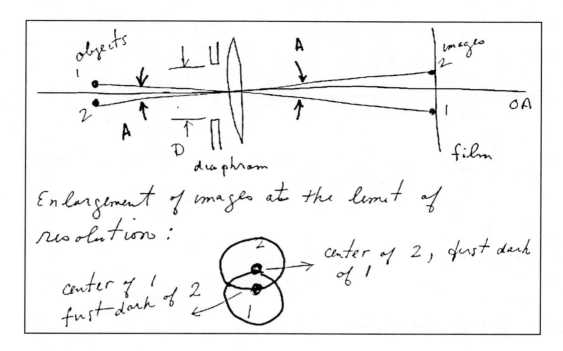

It follows that the smallest angle A between two points of light that can be distinguished by this criterion is

$$A_{min} = \lambda/D,$$

where λ is the wavelength of the light and D is the diameter of the aperture of the lens system.

- The f-stop of a lens system and the minimum angle of resolution. Consider a 50 mm lens with an f-stop of 2. What is the minimum angle of resolution of the lens for light of wavelength 600 nm?

$$\text{f-stop} = \frac{\text{focal length}}{\text{Aperture}} = \frac{50\,mm}{D}$$

$$D = \frac{\text{focal length}}{\text{f-stop}} = \frac{50\,mm}{2} = 25\,mm$$

$$A_{min} = \frac{\lambda}{D} = \frac{600 \times 10^{-9}\,m}{25 \times 10^{-3}\,m} = 2.4 \times 10^{-5}\,\text{radians}$$

A picture is taken using this lens system of a complex pattern 10 meters from the lens. How close together can two points in the pattern be to be resolved by the photograph?

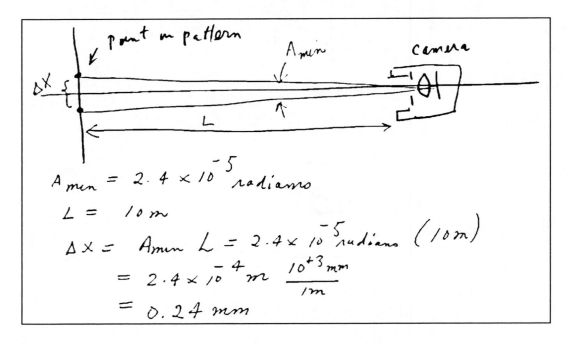

$$A_{min} = 2.4 \times 10^{-5} \text{ radians}$$

$$L = 10 \, m$$

$$\Delta x = A_{min} L = 2.4 \times 10^{-5} \text{ radians} \, (10 \, m)$$

$$= 2.4 \times 10^{-4} \, m \, \frac{10^{+3} \, mm}{1 \, m}$$

$$= 0.24 \, mm$$

CHAPTER 12

Electricity

1. The electromagnetic nature of light.

We have encountered waves that transmit energy in various media:

Visual: transverse waves on a string or slinky having speeds that depend on the density of the string and its tension;

Sound: longitudinal waves in air, water or solids having speeds that depend on the nature of the medium and its temperature;

Light: transverse waves that move in space with a constant speed $c = 3 \times 10^8$ m/s and requires no medium.

All waves satisfy the equation

$$\lambda f = v,$$

where λ is the wavelength, f the frequency and v the speed of the wave. But why does light, or electromagnetic radiation need no medium? The answer is that space can be filled with a "field." This field is real and carries energy, and the energy can be transferred to particles to make them move. In general this field has two parts – electrical and magnetic.

In fact gravity has similar properties – it is a field which travels with the speed as light but its nature is not as well understood as that of the electric and magnetic fields.

---

2.   Comparison of the electric and gravitational fields

a)   The gravitational field and its effect.

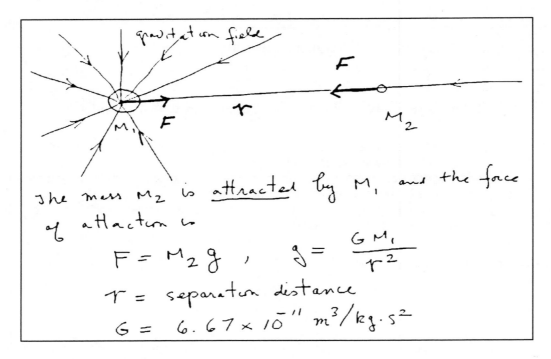

The mass M_2 is <u>attracted</u> by M_1 and the force of attraction is

$$F = M_2 g, \qquad g = \frac{G M_1}{r^2}$$

$$r = \text{separation distance}$$

$$G = 6.67 \times 10^{-11} \ m^3/kg \cdot s^2$$

b)   The electric field and its effect. Electric charge.

Just as the gravitational field acts on mass, the electric and magnetic fields act on charge. Charge is another primary characteristic of matter (as is mass), but unlike mass it comes in two flavors (positive and negative as discovered by Benjamin Franklin):

Electron: $m_e = 9.11 \times 10^{-31}$ kg,

$Q_e = \text{charge} = -e = -1.602 \times 10^{-19}$ coulombs (C);

Proton: $m_P = 1.67 \times 10^{-27}$ kg,

$q_p = \text{charge} = +e = 1.602 \times 10^{-19}$ coulombs (C);

Neutron: $m_P = 1.68 \times 10^{-27}$ kg,

$q_n = \text{charge} = 0;$

The physical constants of nature that we have encountered so far, c and e, have strange values that are absolutely essential to the way the world is structured (including the existence of life).

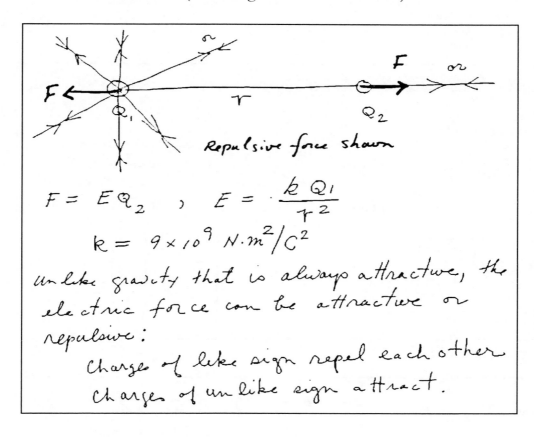

$$F = EQ_2 \quad , \quad E = \frac{kQ_1}{r^2}$$

$$k = 9 \times 10^9 \ N \cdot m^2/C^2$$

Unlike gravity that is always attractive, the electric force can be attractive or repulsive:

Charges of like sign repel each other
Charges of unlike sign attract.

A comparison of the electric and gravitational fields and their effect reveals that

- The electric field can be attractive or repulsive while gravity is only attractive.
- The electric field is vastly stronger than the gravitational field – compare G and k, difference of 10^{20}.

3.   Illustrations and examples.

a) Charging an object.

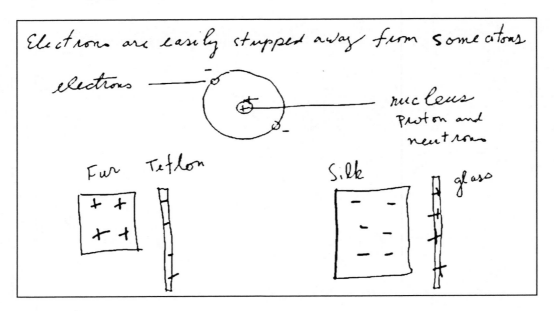

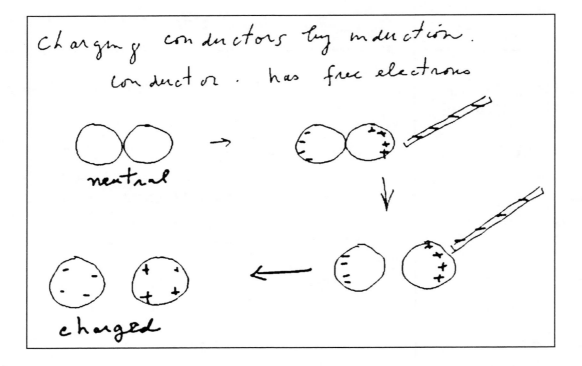

b) Example 1.

A glass rod is rubbed with silk and electrons are removed. How many electrons will give rise to an excess positive charge on the rod of Q = 110 nC (nC = 10^{-9} coulomb).

$$\text{Number of electrons} = \frac{\text{Total charge}}{|\text{charge on an electron}|}$$

$$= \frac{110 \times 10^{-9} \, C}{1.6 \times 10^{-19} \, C} = 6.9 \times 10^{11} \text{ electrons}$$

c) Example 2.

A cork ball is covered with a conducting paint and charged to -2×100^{-11} C. It is touched by another identical ball that is neutral initially. The balls are separated. A third a third neutral ball that is identical to the first two, and the second next touch the second ball and third balls are separated. What is the charge on each ball?

$$Q_1 = -2 \times 10^{-11} C$$

$$Q_1' + Q_2' = -2 \times 10^{-11} C$$

$$Q_1' = Q_2'$$

$$\Rightarrow Q_1' = -1 \times 10^{-11} C$$

$$Q_1' \quad Q_1' = Q_2'$$

$$Q_2' = -1 \times 10^{-11} C$$

$$Q_2'' + Q_3'' = -1 \times 10^{-11} C$$

$$Q_3'' = Q_2'' = -0.5 \times 10^{-11} C$$

4.   The electric field and the electric force

a) Comparison of the gravitational field and the electric field for the hydrogen atom.

Hydrogen is the most abundant atomic structure in the universe and consists of a proton ($m_p = 1.67 \times 10^{-27}$ kg, $q_p = e$) nucleus and an electron ($m_e = 9.11 \times 10^{-31}$ kg and $q_e = -e$) separated by 5.29×10^{-11} m. The electron resides somewhere in an orbit around the nucleus like a planet about the sun, and the diameter of the orbit (the size of hydrogen) is 10.6×10^{-11} m.

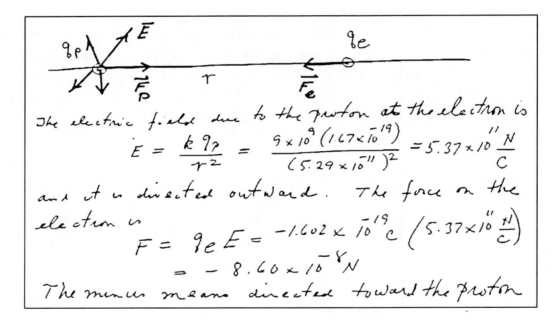

The electric field due to the proton at the electron is

$$E = \frac{k\, q_p}{r^2} = \frac{9 \times 10^9 \left(1.67 \times 10^{-19}\right)}{\left(5.29 \times 10^{-11}\right)^2} = 5.37 \times 10^{11}\,\frac{N}{C}$$

and it is directed outward. The force on the electron is

$$F = q_e E = -1.602 \times 10^{-19}\,C \left(5.37 \times 10^{11}\,\frac{N}{C}\right)$$

$$= -8.60 \times 10^{-8}\,N$$

The minus means directed toward the proton

A gravitational field also exists in the same space, and it also produces an attractive force on the electron:

The gravitational field due to the proton at the electron is

$$g = -\frac{G\, m_p}{r^2} = -\frac{6.67 \times 10^{-11} (1.67 \times 10^{-27})}{(5.29 \times 10^{-11})^2} = -3.98 \times 10^{-17} \frac{N}{kg}$$

and it is directed inward. The grav. force is

$$F = m_e\, g = 9.11 \times 10^{-31} (-3.98 \times 10^{-17})$$
$$= -3.67 \times 10^{-47} N.$$

The minus means directed toward the proton

The two forces are attractive but the electric force is 10^{39} times larger. Even at the event horizon of a black hole of radius 3km and mass 2×10^{30} kg, the gravitational force is about 2.5×10^{-14} N, still smaller that the electric force in the hydrogen atom.

The electric force completely overwhelms the gravitational force except when the electric field is absent due to a neutral charge or when the distances are even smaller than the event horizon of a black hole – for example, the universe at the time of the "Big Bang."

b) Coulomb's law.

The combination F = q1 E is called Coulomb's law:

$$F = q_1\, E = q_1\, (k\, q_2 / r^2) = k\, q_1\, q_2 / r^2.$$

This is a vector equation. The force on charge q_1 due to charge q_2 (and vise versa) is either directed outward (away from the other charge) or inward depending on the signs of the charges – like charges repel and unlike charges attract.

c) Example of Coulomb's law.

Two charges $q_1 = 2 \times 10^{-8}$ C and $q_2 = 6 \times 10^{-8}$ C are separated by a distance of 30 cm. What is the force on each of the charges?

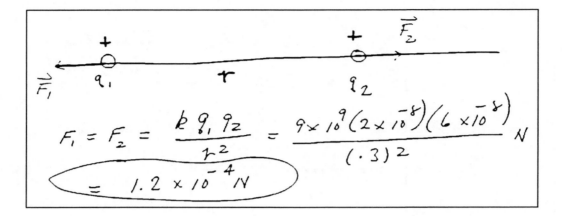

$$F_1 = F_2 = \frac{k\, q_1\, q_2}{r^2} = \frac{9 \times 10^9 \left(2 \times 10^{-8}\right)\left(6 \times 10^{-8}\right)}{(.3)^2} \; N$$

$$= 1.2 \times 10^{-4} \; N$$

A third charge $q_3 = -2 \times 10^{-8}$ C is placed at the midpoint between these two charges. What force does it experience?

$$F_{31} = \frac{k\, q_1\, q_3}{.15 m^2} = \frac{9 \times 10^9 \left(2 \times 10^{-8}\right)\left(-2 \times 10^{-8}\right)}{.15^2} \; N$$

$$= -1.6 \times 10^{-4} N$$

$$F_{32} = \frac{k\, q_3\, q_2}{.15 m^2} = \frac{9 \times 10^9 \left(-2 \times 10^{-8}\right)\left(6 \times 10^{-8}\right)}{.15^2}$$

$$= +4.8 \times 10^{-4} N$$

$$F_{TOTAL} = -1.6 \times 10^{-4} + 4.8 \times 10^{-4} = 3.2 \times 10^{-4} N$$

Therefore, there is a net force on q_3 to the right of magnitude 3.2×10^{-4} N.

Where can the third charge be placed so that there is no force on the charge? First note if the charge is placed outside the two fixed charges, there cannot be any cancellation. For example, if the third charge is to the right of both fixed charges, the force from each will be to the left. It follows that the third charge has to be somewhere in between:

$$F_{13} = -\frac{k|q_1 q_3|}{a^2} \quad , \quad F_{32} = +\frac{k|q_3||q_2|}{b^2}$$

$$F_{13} + F_{32} = 0$$

$$\rightarrow -\frac{k|q_1||q_3|}{a^2} + \frac{k|q_3||q_2|}{b^2} = 0$$

$$-|q_1| b^2 + |q_2| a^2 = 0 \quad \rightarrow \quad a^2/b^2 = \left|\frac{q_1}{q_2}\right| = \frac{2}{6} = \frac{1}{3}$$

$$a/b = \frac{1}{\sqrt{3}} = \frac{1}{1.732}$$

Also,
$$a + b = 0.3 \, m$$

$$\rightarrow a + 1.732 a = .3 \, m \rightarrow a = \frac{.3}{2.732} = .110 \, m$$

---

5.   **Electric field, electrical potential energy and voltage.**

---

a) The electric field in two-dimensional space.

Consider the two fixed positive charges each of value 2×10^{-8} C. They are fixed on the x axis a distance of 30 cm apart. What is the electric field produced by these two charges at the center and at a point 15 cm above the center?

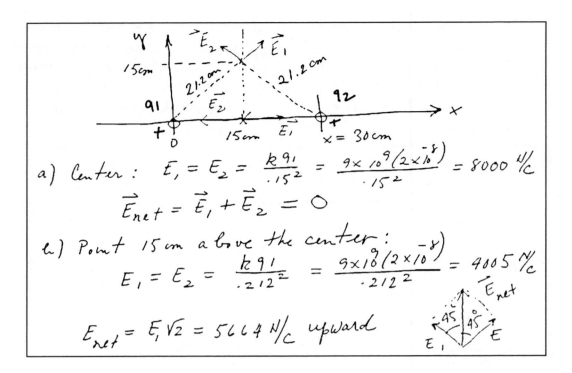

$$a)\ \text{Center}:\ E_1 = E_2 = \frac{k\,q_1}{.15^2} = \frac{9 \times 10^9 (2 \times 10^{-8})}{.15^2} = 8000\ \text{N/c}$$

$$\vec{E}_{net} = \vec{E}_1 + \vec{E}_2 = 0$$

$b)$ Point 15 cm above the center:

$$E_1 = E_2 = \frac{k\,q_1}{.212^2} = \frac{9 \times 10^9 (2 \times 10^{-8})}{.212^2} = 4005\ \text{N/c}$$

$$E_{net} = E_1 \sqrt{2} = 5664\ \text{N/c}\ \text{upward}$$

If the third charge $q_3 = -2 \times 10^{-8}\,\text{C}$ is placed first at the center and next at the above point, what is the force on this charge at these two points.

$$\vec{F} = q_3 \vec{E}_{net}$$

$a)$ At the center,
$$\vec{F} = q_3 \vec{E}_{net} = 0$$

$b)$ At the point above
$$F = q_3 E_{net} = 2 \times 10^{-8}\,\text{C}\,(5664\ \text{N/c})$$
$$= 1.13 \times 10^{-4}\ \text{N}\ \text{downward}$$

If an external force moves this third charge from the center to the point above the center, the external force would have to be upward to counteract the electric force. At the result energy would have to be expended, and the charge q_3 held at the upper point would have and electrical potential energy. If it were released, it would move toward the center just as a mass moves toward the ground when released from a height.

b) The analogy with gravity extended – the constant electric field.

The electric field between two charge conducting plates where the top plate has a total charge +Q and the lower plate has the charge –Q.

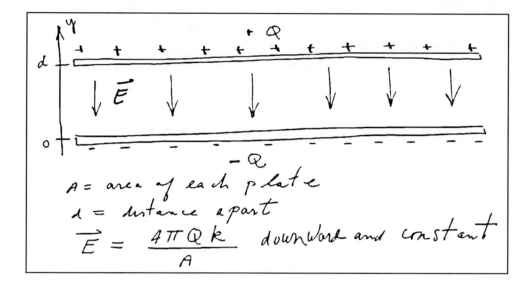

$$A = \text{area of each plate}$$
$$d = \text{distance apart}$$
$$\vec{E} = \frac{4\pi Q k}{A} \quad \text{downward and constant}$$

c) The potential energy of a positive charge placed between the plates using the bottom positive plate as the reference level.

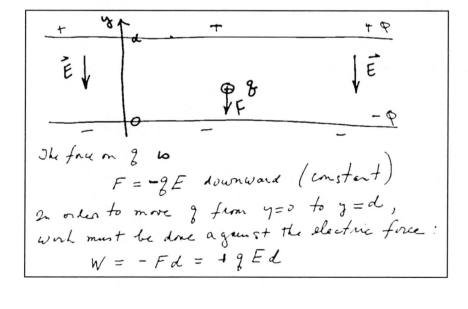

The force on q is

$$F = -qE \quad \text{downward (constant)}$$

In order to move q from $y=0$ to $y=d$, work must be done against the electric force:

$$W = -Fd = +qEd$$

The work done against the electric force to move the charge from y = 0 to y is called the electric potential energy:

$$U_{el} = q\,E\,y, \text{ unit} = \text{joule}.$$

Remember that for gravity above the surface of the earth where the gravitational field is g (downward), the potential energy of a mass m a distance y above the ground is

$$U_{gr} = m\,g\,y.$$

For the parallel plate example, the **potential or voltage** of the charge a distance y above the lower plate is defined as

$$V = U_{el} / q$$
$$= E\,y, \text{ unit} = \text{joule/coulomb} = \text{volt}.$$

The voltage at the bottom plate is zero and the voltage at the top plates is Ed. The voltage difference between the top and bottom plates is V = E d. The potential varies opposite the direction of the electric field E – so it falls or decreases in the direction of E.

d) Example.

Two parallel plates are charged so that the potential difference across the plates is 1000 volts. The separation of the plates is d = 5 cm, and the area of each plate is A = 0.5 m². The upper plate is high potential.

- What is the electric field between the plates (magnitude and direction)?
- What is the charge on each plate and which is positive?
- A point charge and mass of $q = -5 \times 10^{-8}$ C and m = 1 gram is placed in halfway between the plates. What is the force on this charge and it potential energy?
- What is the gravitational force on the particle?

a) $V = Ed$

$E = \dfrac{1000 \text{ Volts}}{.05m}$

$= 20,000 \dfrac{V}{m}$

or $20,000 \text{ N/c}$

downward

c) $E = \dfrac{4\pi Q}{A}$, $+Q$ on top

$Q = \dfrac{EA}{4\pi k} = \dfrac{(2\times10^4)(.5)}{4\pi 9\times10^9} C = 8.84\times10^{-8} C$

c) Force on the charge q:

$F = qE = 5\times10^{-8} C \left(2\times10^4 \dfrac{N}{C}\right) = 1.0\times10^{-3} N$ downward

Potential energy of the charge q:

$U_{el} = qE\dfrac{d}{2} = \left(5\times10^{-8}C\right) 2\times10^4 \dfrac{N}{C} \left(2.5\times10^{-2} m\right)$

$= 25\times10^{-6} \text{ joules}$

d) The gravitational force is

$F_g = mg = 10^{-3} kg \left(10\, m/s^2\right) = 10^{-2} \text{ joules}$

downward

---

6. The constant electric field and conservation of energy.

a) Basic equations for the motion of particles in a constant electric field.

$\vec{F} = q\vec{E}$; $q>0$ $\vec{F}$ is along $\vec{E}$

$q<0$ $\vec{F}$ is opposite $\vec{E}$.

$U_B - U_A = \Delta U =$ change in potential energy

$= -F\Delta x = -qE\Delta x$

where $\Delta x = x_B - x_A$.

Note that

$\Delta U = U_B - U_A > 0$ if $q < 0$,

$\Delta U < 0$ if $q > 0$.

The electric potential (unit = volt) is defined in terms of the potential energy as

$$\Delta V = V_B - V_A = \Delta U / q = - E \, \Delta x.$$

The potential always decreases in the direction of the electric field.

As the electric force is conservative, like gravity, the total energy of a charge moving because of the electric force is constant if there is not friction:

$$\text{Energy} = K + U, K = \tfrac{1}{2} \, m \, v^2,$$

or

$$K_A + U_A = K_B + K_B.$$

b) Example 1.

A proton is released from rest near the positive plate of a parallel plate system. Each plate has an area of $0.25 \, m^2$, the distance between the plates is d = 10 cm and the plates are charged to 1500 volts.

- What is the charge on each plate?
- What is the force on the proton anywhere between the plates?
- If the positive plate is the reference position of the proton, what is its electric potential energy at x = 0 and at x = d? Note that the potential decreases in the direction of the electric field, so the potential energy of the proton, q V, decreases as the proton moves from x = 0 to x = d.
- What is the kinetic energy of the proton just before it hits the negative plate?
- What is the velocity of the proton just before it hits the negative plate?

a) $E = \dfrac{V}{d}$

$= \dfrac{1500 \text{ Volts}}{.1 m}$

$= 15,000 \text{ V/m} \left(\dfrac{J}{cm}\right)$

To the right

$E = \dfrac{4\pi k \varphi}{A}$

$\varphi = \dfrac{EA}{4\pi k} = \dfrac{15,000 \frac{J}{C} (.25 m^2)}{4\pi \; 9\times10^9 \; Nm^2/c^2}$

$= 3.32 \times 10^{-8} C$

high pot ... Low Potential

$+Q$ proton $-\varphi$

$\rightarrow E$

0 $\xrightarrow{F}$ d $\rightarrow x$

$\rightarrow$

1500 volts $\rightarrow$ ... $\leftarrow 0$ volts

b) $F = q_p E = 1.602 \times 10^{-19} C \left(15,000 \frac{J}{C}\right) = 2.4 \times 10^{-15} N$

to the right

c) $U_{x=0} = q_{proton} V = 1500 \text{ volts} \left(1.602 \times 10^{-19} C\right) = 2.40 \times 10^{-16} J$

$U_{x=d} = q_{proton} V = 0$

d) $E_{x=0} = E_{x=d}$

$U_{x=0} + K_{x=0}^{\nearrow 0} = U_{x=d}^{\nearrow 0} + K_{x=d} \rightarrow K_{x=d} = 2.40 \times 10^{-16} J$

e) $K_{x=d} = 2.4 \times 10^{-16} J = \frac{1}{2} m_p v^2$

$= \frac{1}{2} \left(1.67 \times 10^{-27} kg\right) v^2$

$\rightarrow v = \left[\dfrac{2(2.4 \times 10^{-16})}{1.67 \times 10^{-27}}\right]^{1/2} = 5.36 \times 10^5 \text{ m/s}$

- If an electron is released from rest from the negative plate, what is its velocity just before it hits the positive plate?

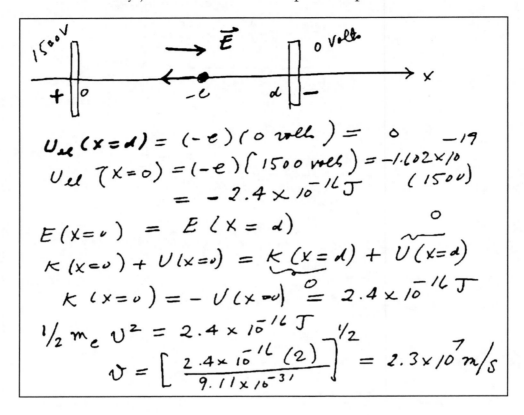

$U_{el}(x=d) = (-e)(0 \text{ volts}) = 0$

$U_{el}(x=0) = (-e)(1500 \text{ volts}) = -1.602 \times 10^{-19} (1500)$

$\qquad = -2.4 \times 10^{-16} J$

$E(x=0) = E(x=d)$

$K(x=0) + U(x=0) = K(x=d) + U(x=d)$

$K(x=0) = -U(x=0) = 2.4 \times 10^{-16} J$

$\frac{1}{2} m_e v^2 = 2.4 \times 10^{-16} J$

$v = \left[\dfrac{2.4 \times 10^{-16}(2)}{9.11 \times 10^{-31}} \right]^{1/2} = 2.3 \times 10^7 \, m/s$

c) Example 2.

Two parallel plates are shown. The top plate has a charge $Q = 5 \times 10^{-7}$ C and the bottom plate has a chare $-Q$. The plates are a distance of 5 cm apart. A = 0.5 m².

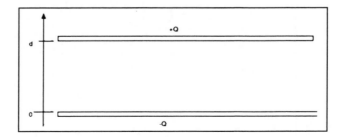

- What is the electric field between the plates? Give the magnitude and the direction.
- What is the potential difference between the plates, and which plate is at the higher potential?

- A particle of mass M and charge q = −2 × 10⁻⁸ C is placed near the bottom negative plate. What is the magnitude and the direction of the electric force on this charge?
- If the charge q is released from rest near the bottom plate, what is its kinetic energy just before it hits the top plate?
- If the plate are near the surface of the earth (g = 10 m/s²), what mass M would allow the particle to remain suspended between the plates?

a) $E = \dfrac{4\pi k Q}{A} = \dfrac{4\pi(9\times 10^9)5\times 10^{-7}}{.5} \dfrac{N}{C} = 1.13\times 10^5 \dfrac{N}{C}$

$\underline{down}$

b) $V = Ed = 1.13\times 10^5 \, N/C \, (.5m) = 5650 \, volts$

The positive plate is the high potential side —

$V(top) = 5650 \, volts, \quad V(bottom) = 0.$

c) $F = |qE| = 2\times 10^{-8}(1.13\times 10^5) = 2.26\times 10^{-3} \, N$

upward (opposite $\vec{E}$)

d) $U(bottom) = qV = -2\times 10^{-8}C(0 \, volts) = 0$

$U(top) = -2\times 10^{-8}C(5650 \, volts) = -1.13\times 10^{-4}$ joules

$\underbrace{U(bottom)}_{0} + \underbrace{k(bottom)}_{0} = \underbrace{U(top)}_{-1.13\times 10^{-4}J} + k(top)$

$k(top) = 1.13\times 10^{-4}$ joules

e)

$W = mg = m \, 10 \, m/s^2 = |qE| = 2\times 10^{-8}\left(1.13\times 10^5 \dfrac{N}{C}\right)$

$m = \dfrac{2\times 10^{-8}(1.13\times 10^5)}{10} kg = 2.26\times 10^{-4} \, kg$

$= 0.226 \, grams$

d) Example 3.

The electric potential energy of an object at point A is 50 joules. If it is released from rest at A, it gains 30 joules of kinetic energy as it reaches point B. What is the potential energy at B? If the object has a charge of 2 C, what is the potential difference between A and B?

$$U(A) = 50 \text{ J}, \quad K(A) = 0 \text{ (released from rest)}$$

$$U(B) = ? \quad, \quad K(B) = 30 \text{ J}$$

$$\underbrace{U(A)}_{50\text{ J}} + \underbrace{K(A)}_{=0} = U(B) + \underbrace{K(B)}_{30\text{ J}}$$

$$U(B) = 50 \text{ J} - 30 \text{ J} = 20 \text{ J}$$

$$V_B - V_A = q(U_B - U_A) = 2C(20\text{ J} - 50 \text{ J})$$

$$= -60 \text{ volts}$$

e) Example 4.

Points A and B each have an electric potential of 6 volts. How much work is required to take 3 mC of charge from A to B?

$$V_A = 6 \text{ volts} \qquad V_B = 6 \text{ volts}$$

$$U_A = q V_A \; , \quad U_B = q V_B$$

Work required to move q from A to B

$$= U_B - U_A = q(V_B - V_A) = 0$$

Electric Circuits and Ohm's Law

1.	Electric current.

The convention is that current is the motion of positive charge, so the "current" moves from A to B (the actual electron flow is from B to A). Example: in a copper wire of of radius 9×10^{-4} m, there are 8.49×10^{28} free electrons per unit volume of the wire. The electric current in the wire is I = 17 mA (1.7×10^{-2} A). What is the speed of the electrons?

$$I = (\text{electrons/volume})(\text{charge on electron})$$

$$\times \mathcal{V} \text{ Area of wire}$$

$$1.7 \times 10^{-2} A = 8.49 \times 10^{24} \frac{\text{electron}}{\text{volume}} \left(1.602 \times 10^{-19} C\right)$$

$$\times \mathcal{V} \left(\pi \left(9 \times 10^{-4} m\right)^2 \right)$$

$$\mathcal{V} = \frac{\left(1.7 \times 10^{-2}\right)}{8.49 \times 10^{24} \left(1.6 \times 10^{-19}\right) \pi \left(81 \times 10^{-4}\right)}$$

$$= 4.9 \times 10^{-7} m/s$$

Suppose that the wire is stretch a distance of 10 m across a room, and the switch for the current is pushed at time t=0. First, an electric field moves across the wire at the speed of light, so it takes $10m/(3 \times 10^8 \text{ m/s}) = 3.33 \times 10^{-8}$ seconds to move the length of the wire. However, the electrons take $10m/(4.9 \times 10^{-7} \text{ m/s}) = 2.04 \times 10^7$ seconds to move across along the wire. This is nearly a year.

2.   Resistance.

The free electrons that move through a wire at a snail's pace are moving at a constant speed. Since they feel an electric force, a resistive force must be present to slow them down. This resistance then removes electrical energy from the system of moving charges and is realized as heat (similar to friction).

3.   A simple loop circuit.

The circuit contains a source of energy (battery) and resistance.

a) Schematic representation.

First, a cartoon of the physical situation is presented:

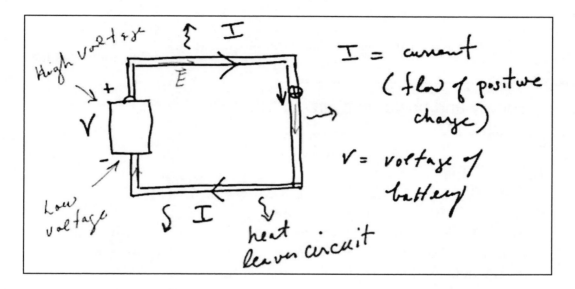

Next, the schematic circuit diagram is presented:

---

4.   Ohm's law.

For certain materials like copper, silver, aluminum and iron, the current in the circuit is proportional to the voltage of the battery. The constant of proportionality is called the "resistance" of the circuit. This relationship is called Ohm's law:

$$V = I\,R, \quad R = \text{resistance},$$
$$\text{unit} = \text{volts/(ampere)} = \text{ohm } (\Omega).$$

5.   Energy and power in a circuit.

a) Power in:

$V = \Delta V$ = voltage across the battery,
$\Delta U = \Delta q\,\Delta V$ = change in the potential energy of a positive charge Δq as it moves from the positive terminal to the negative terminal = energy delivered to the circuit by the battery
Pin = Power delivered by the battery
$\quad = \Delta U/\Delta t = \Delta q\,\Delta V/\Delta t = \Delta V\,(\Delta q/\Delta t)$
Pin = V I.

b) Power out:

$$P_{out} = P_{in} = I\,V = I\,(IR) = I^2\,R$$
$$P_{out} = I^2\,R.$$

The unit of power is joule/second = watt

c) Example:

A 100 watt light blub is connected to a 110 volt battery. What is the current in the circuit and its resistance?

$V = 110 \text{ volts}$

$R = \text{resistance of blub}$

$I = \text{current}$

$V = IR = 110 \text{ volts}$

$P_{out} = 100 \text{ watts} = I^2 R$

$\rightarrow I^2 \left(\frac{110}{I} \right) = 100 \rightarrow I = \frac{100}{110} = \boxed{0.909 \text{ amp}}$

$R = \frac{110}{.909} = \boxed{121 \, \Omega}$

---

6. A circuit with series resistors. Equivalent resistance.

$I = \text{current in both resistors}$

$P_{in} = VI$

$P_{out} = I^2 R_1 + I^2 R_2$

$\overline{P_{in} = VI}$

$P_{out} = I^2 R_{eq}$

$I^2 R_{eq} = I^2 R_1 + I^2 R_2 \rightarrow \boxed{R_{eq} = R_1 + R_2}$

equivalent circuit

For resistors in series, the current through each resistor is the same, and the equivalent resistance is just the sum of the individual resistances:

$$R_{equivanent} = R1 + R2 + R3 + ...$$

---

7.   Electrical circuit applications.

a) Series and parallel arrangements of resistors.

- Series.

The current through each resistor is I.

$$I R_1 = V_a - V_b$$
$$I R_2 = V_b - V_c$$
$$I R_3 = V_c - V_d$$
$$I R_4 = V_d - V_e$$

$$V = V_a - V_e = I R_{eq}$$

$$(V_a - V_e) + (V_b - V_b) + (V_c - V_d) + (V_d - V_e) = V_a - V_e$$

$$I R_1 + I R_2 + I R_3 + I R_4 = I R_{eq}$$

$$R_{eq} = R_1 + R_2 + R_3 + R_4$$

$$V = I \, Req,$$
$$R_{eq} = R1 + R2 + R3 + ...$$

- Parallel.

The electric potential at all points "a" is the same (high). The electric potential at all points "b" is the same (low or zero).

The voltage across each resistor is the same:

$$V_{ab} = V = V_a - V_b$$

The current I divides through the resistors

$$I = I_1 + I_2,$$

where

$$I_1 R_1 = V \quad, \quad I_2 R_2 = V$$

For the equivalent circuit,

$$V = I R_{eq}$$

$$\rightarrow \quad I = \frac{V}{R_{eq}} = I_1 + I_2 = \frac{V}{R_1} + \frac{V}{R_2}$$

$$\rightarrow \quad \frac{1}{R_{eq}} = \frac{1}{R_1} + \frac{1}{R_2}$$

For resistors in parallel,

$$V = I R_{eq},$$
$$1/Req = 1/R_1 + 1/R_2 + 1/R_3 + \dots$$

b) Example 1.

Circuit reduction. Reduce the following circuit containing 7 resistors in series-parallel arrangements to a single equivalent resistance and find its value:

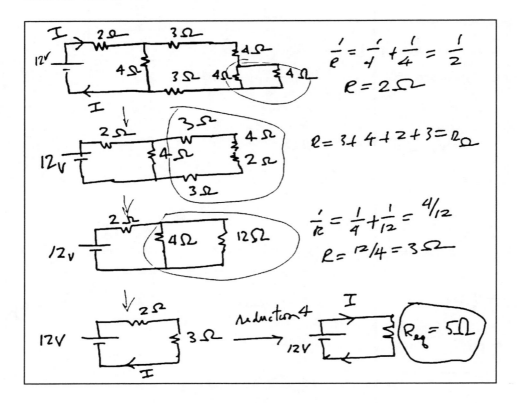

The equivalent resistor is 5 Ω, the current drawn form the battery is I R_{eq} = V, or I = 12 volts / 5 ohms = 2.4 amps. The power delivered to the circuit by the battery is Pin = I V = 2.4 amps x 12 volts = 28.8 watts. If we determined the current in each resistor, we would find that the sum of all the powers out of the seven resistors would be 28.8 watts.

c) Example 2.

Circuit containing two batteries. For the circuit below, find the currents I_1 and I_2, the power delivered by the batteries.

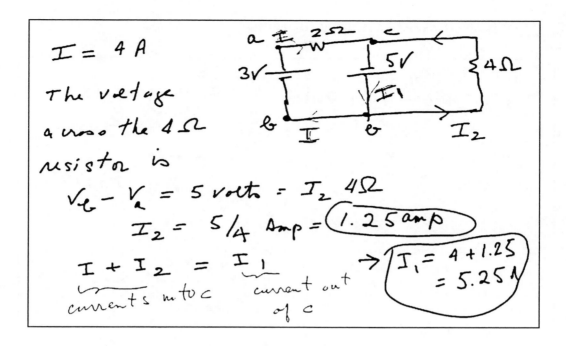

$I = 4\,A$

The voltage across the 4Ω resistor is

$$V_c - V_a = 5\ \text{volts} = I_2\, 4\Omega$$

$$I_2 = 5/4\ \text{Amp} = 1.25\ \text{amp}$$

$$I + I_2 = I_1 \rightarrow I_1 = 4 + 1.25 = 5.25\,A$$

currents into c   current out of c

The power delivered by the two batteries is:

$$P_{\text{in by 3V}} = IV = 4\ \text{amps} \times 3\ \text{volts} = 12\ \text{watts}$$

$$P_{\text{in by 5 V}} = IV = 5.25\ \text{amps} \times 5\ \text{volts} = 26.25\ \text{watts}.$$

The power consumed by the two resistors is:

$$P_{\text{out in 2 ohm}} = I^2 R = (4\ \text{amps})^2 \times 2\ \text{ohms} = 32\ \text{watts},$$

$$P_{\text{out in 4 ohm}} = I^2 R = (1.25\ \text{amps})^2 \times 4\ \text{ohms} = 6.25\ \text{watts}.$$

We see that power in by the batteries equals the power out in the resistors.

Power is always lost in resistors ($I^2 R$). If the current through a battery is out of the plus terminal, then the battery delivers power (IV). If current us forced through a battery into is plus terminal, then the battery consumes power (−IV).

d) Example 3.

A 1500 watt heater for a sauna requires 1 hour to heat the water to 190 degrees F. Electricity costs $0.12 / kwh.

What is the cost of heating the sauna?

$$P_{out} = I^2 R = 1500 \text{ watts}$$

$$1 \, kWh = 1000 \frac{J}{s} \, (3600 \, s)$$

$V = 110 \text{ Volts}$

$$= 3.6 \times 10^6 \text{ Joules} \checkmark$$

$$\text{Energy needed} = 1500 \frac{J}{s} \, (60 \, min) \frac{60 \, s}{min}$$

$$= 5.4 \times 10^6 \text{ Joules}$$

$$Cost = \frac{\$ \, 0.12}{kWh} \left(\frac{5.4}{3.6} \, kWh \text{ needed} \right) = 18 \text{ cents}$$

Find the current drawn from the circuit and the resistance of the heater.

$$I^2 R = 1500 \text{ watts}$$

$$IV = I \, 110 \text{ volts} = 1500 \text{ watts}$$

$$\rightarrow \quad I = \frac{1500}{110} \, A = 13.6 \, \underline{A}$$

$$R = \frac{1500}{(13.6)^2} \, ohm = 8.11 \, \Omega$$

The Magnetic Field and Electromagnetism

1. The creation of magnetic fields by electric currents.

a) Circular loops of current.

$$B = \frac{M_0 \, I \, N}{2R}, \qquad M_0 = 1.26 \times 10^{-6} \frac{Tm}{amp}$$

$$\text{unit} = \text{teola} \quad (T)$$

$N = $ number of turns

$R = $ radius of loop

b) A long straight wire of current.

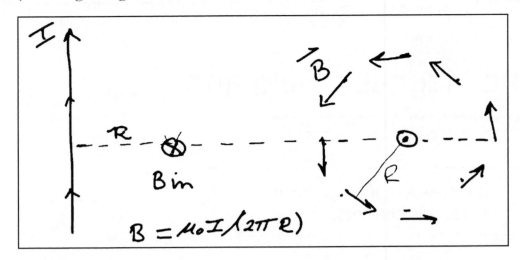

$$B = \mu_0 I / (2\pi R)$$

c) Solenoid of current.

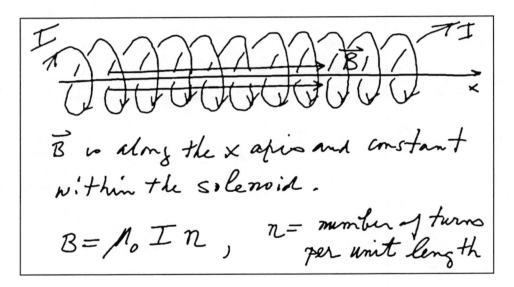

$\vec{B}$ is along the x axis and constant within the solenoid.

$$B = \mu_0 I n , \quad n = \frac{\text{number of turns}}{\text{per unit length}}$$

d) Permanent magnet.

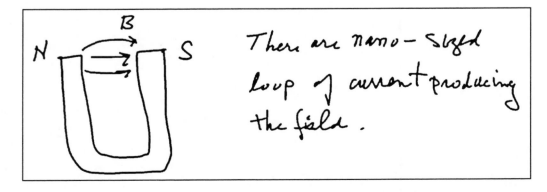

There are nano-sized loop of current producing the field.

In all these examples, moving charge (current) produces magnetic fields. The solenoid produces a constant B field so it is a useful device. Recall that parallel charged produce a constant E field, so by a combination of solenoids and parallel plates, one can create crossed E and B fields. We will discuss the consequences of that next.

2.	The magnetic force.

We argued that the electric field is real as it fills space with an energy that can exert forces on charged particles. In a similar way, the magnetic field fills space with energy that can exert forces on charged particles, but the charges need to move in order for this to happen.

$\vec{v}$ = velocity of charge q along y

$\vec{B}$ = magnetic field along z

$\vec{F}$ = magnetic force on q along x

$$F = q v B$$

3. The motion of a charged particle moving
   through constant electric and magnetic fields.

a) A constant electric field.

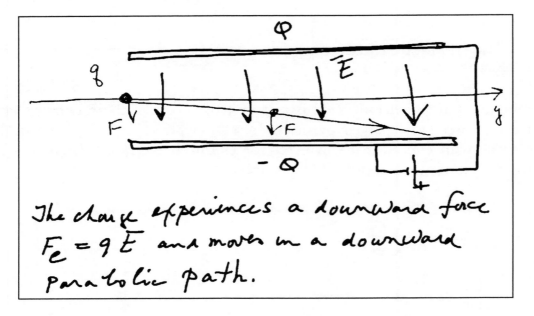

The charge experiences a downward force
$F_e = q E$ and moves in a downward
parabolic path.

b) A constant magnetic field.

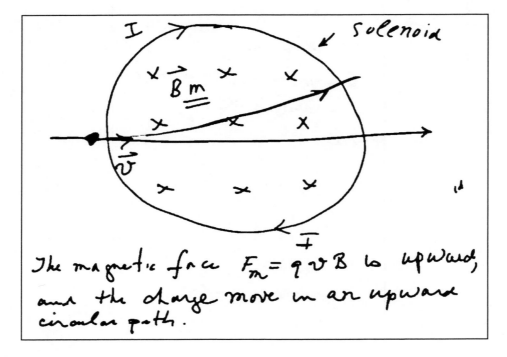

The magnetic force $F_m = q v B$ is upward,
and the charge move in an upward
circular path.

c) Combination of E and B fields adjusted so that the charge moves through the space of the fields without deflection.

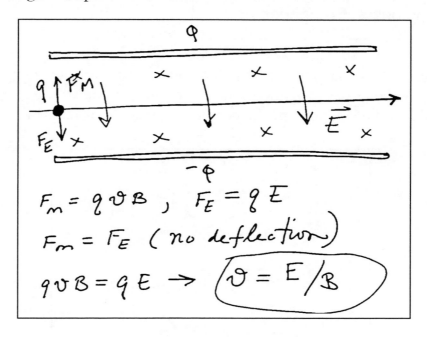

$$F_m = q \vartheta B \; , \quad F_E = q E$$

$$F_m = F_E \; (\text{no deflection})$$

$$q \vartheta B = q E \; \rightarrow \; \boxed{\vartheta = E / B}$$

d) Example.

Parallel conducting plates arranged as above are charged to 10,000 volts, and the plates are a distance d = 50 cm. A magnetic field also exists in the space directed into the page. A particle of charge q = 5 × 10^{-7} C and moving with a speed v = 10^4 m/s moves between the plates with no deflection. What is the magnitude of the magnetic field?

$$E = \frac{V}{d} = \frac{10^4 V}{.5 \, m} = 2 \times 10^4 \; N/c$$

$$\vartheta = E/B = \frac{2 \times 10^4 \, N/c}{B} = 10^4 \, m/s$$

$$\rightarrow B = \frac{2 \times 10^4}{10^4} = \boxed{2 T}$$

4. Motion of a charged particle in a constant magnetic field.

The force on the charge is always perpendicular to the velocity, and this produces a circular path for the particle. The magnitude of the force is F = q v B, and it is directed toward the center of the circle of radius R:

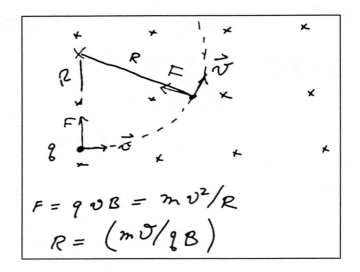

$$F = q\,v\,B = m\,v^2/R$$

$$R = \left(m\,v/q\,B\right)$$

5. Electromagnetic Induction.

a) Faraday's law.

A changing magnetic flux through a conducting loop induces a voltage in the loop (like a battery) given by

$$E = -\,N\,\Delta\Phi/\Delta t,$$

Where N is the number of turns in the loop, the minus sign is a statement of Lenz's law (no runaway current). The term Φ is called the magnetic flux, and:

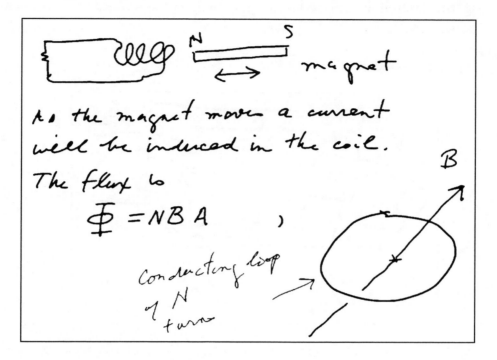

As the magnet moves a current will be induced in the coil. The flux is

$$\Phi = NBA$$

conducting loop of N turns

B

The number of turns in the coil is N.

b) The inductor.

We have introduced three circuit elements: battery, resistor, capacitor. The fourth basic element is called an inductor. In any circuit, no matter how small and high tech has these four passive circuit elements.

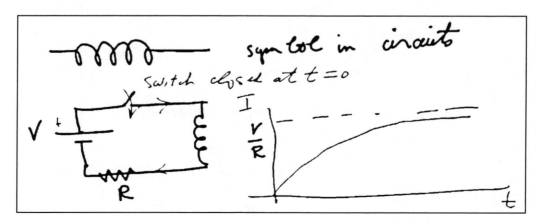

The switch is closed at time t =0. The current builds from zero and
fills the coil with a magnetic field and induces a voltage V in the coil
that opposes the battery. The current reaches a steady value of V/R.
If the switch is opened, the field will collapse and a spark will arc
across the switch.

c) Transformers.

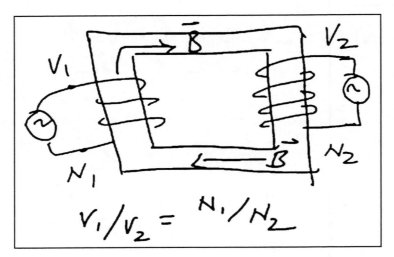

$$V_1/V_2 = N_1/N_2$$

As an example, consider a transformer converts 100 volts to 10 volts.
The 100- volt side has 1000 turns. How many turns are on the low
voltage side? If the current on the low side is 1 amps, what is the
current on the high side?

$$V_1/V_2 = N_1/N_2$$

$$\frac{100 \text{ volts}}{10 \text{ volts}} = \frac{100 \text{ turns}}{N_2}$$

$$N_2 = 10 \text{ turns}$$

Power in = Power out + losses

$$V_1 I_1 = V_2 I_2$$

$$I_1/I_2 = V_2/V_1 = \frac{N_2}{N_1}$$

if $I_2 = 1 \text{ amp}$, $I_1 = (1A)\left(\frac{10}{100}\right) = 0.1 A$

6. Electromagnetic radiation

a) Fields produced by an oscillating dipole.

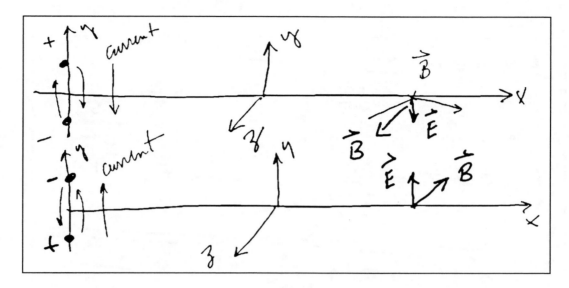

At the point in space we have selected, the electric field oscillates in the positive and negative y directions, and the magnetic field oscillates in the positive and negative z directions. The fields propagate in the x direction with a speed c.

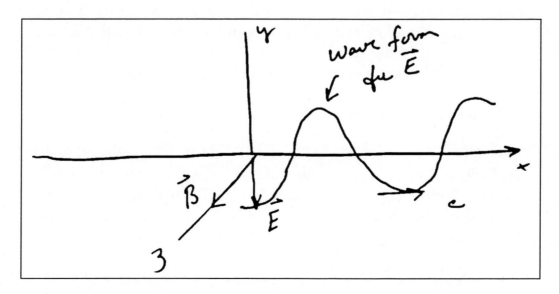

b) The speed of an electromagnetic wave.

The full theory of electricity and magnetism gives rise to this expression for the speed of EM radiation:

$$v = c = 1/\text{sqrt}(\varepsilon_0 \, \mu_0).$$

$$k = 9 \times 10^9 \frac{Nm^2}{c^2} = \frac{1}{4\pi \varepsilon_0}$$

$$\mu_0 = 4\pi \times 10^{-7} \frac{Tm}{A} = 4\pi \times 10^{-7} \frac{Ns^2}{c^2}$$

$$\left(\text{unit of } T\right) = \frac{N}{c\,m/s} \quad (\text{recall } F = qvB)$$

$$c = \frac{1}{\sqrt{10^{-9}/(4\pi 9)\,\frac{c^2}{Nm^2}\,\,4\pi \times 10^{-7}\frac{Ns^2}{c^2}}}$$

$$= 3 \times 10^8 \, m/s$$

An electromagnetic field consists of E and B fields (crossed in dipole radiation). These are traveling waves moving in space with a velocity c. The electric field exerts a force $F = q\,E = ma$ on charges, and the magnetic field exerts a force $q\,v\,B$ on moving charges.

c) Electromagnetic waves.

An electromagnetic wave consists of E and B fields (crossed in dipole radiation). These are traveling waves moving in space with a velocity c. The electric field exerts a force $F = q\,E = ma$ on charges, and the magnetic field exerts a force $q\,v\,B$ on moving charges. As for all waves, $\lambda f = c$.

Drexel's radio station WKDU operates at a frequency of 91.7 MHz. The nominal wavelength of this radiation is

$$\lambda = c/f = 3 \times 10^8 \text{ m/s} / 91.7 \times 10^6 \text{ Hz} = 4.86 \text{ m}.$$

This is a radio wave. The entire spectrum of electro magnetic radiation is

λ (m)	Designation	Energy
10^6		Low
$\downarrow$	Radiowave	
1		
$\downarrow$	microwaves	
10^{-2}		
$\downarrow$	infrared	
10^{-6}		
700 nm	visible	
400 nm		
10^{-8}	ultraviolet	
$\downarrow$		
10^{-10}		
$\downarrow$	x rays	
10^{-12}		High
$\downarrow$	γ rays	

The World View Changes - Special Relativity

1. The death of absolute space.

a) Where is the ether?

We discussed optics, wave interference and fringe patterns for a reason, and that reason is that a beautiful experiment using these techniques killed the classical conception of space and time. The experiment was designed and carried out in 1881 by Albert Michelson and Edward Morley. This is roughly 200 years after the work of Newton and fourteen years before Einstein's work on the special theory of relativity.

It uses an interferometer to form a fringe pattern by combining two rays of light that come together from different directions. At the time, it was assumed that space is absolute and tangible as a medium called the either. Electromagnetic radiation, light, travels in the either like sound in air, and if it travels in the direction of an either wind, light moves faster, and it moves slower if it travels against the either wind. Now the Earth moves with a speed of about 3×10^4 m/s in its orbit around the sun, so if the either is fixed with respect to the sun, there is an either wind of this speed moving across the surface of the earth. Now, consider the Michelson interferometer:

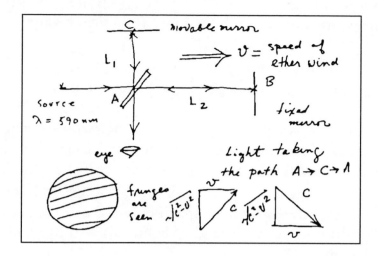

The fringe pattern is formed because light moves with differing speeds with and perpendicular to the either wind, and a calculation of the difference in time along the two paths, assuming that $L_1 = L_2 = L$, is about L/c (v^2/c^2). If the apparatus is rotated by 90 degrees so that the two paths exchange position relative to the either wind, the fringe pattern should shift, and with the numbers given here and L about 1 meter, the shift should be about 0.04 fringe widths- easily seen by this instrument.

However, no shift is seen. The experiment was redone many times by different people using large arm lengths to increase the predicted shift, and no matter what, no shift was seen. This can only mean that there is no either wind - there is no either or space is not absolute.

b) Einstein's special theory of relativity (1905)[10].

Albert Einstein was working as a patent clerk in 1905 and physics in his spare time. In this year he not only explained the above experiment, he also showed that atoms exist (Brownian motion), and he showed that light has a particle nature (photo electric effect). He certainly knew about the Michelson-Morley result, but his motivation was deeper. He saw that Newton's mechanics and Maxwell's theory of electromagnetism were inconsistent, and he opted to believe in the electromagnetic theory. The necessary modification of mechanics will be discussed later, and it led ultimately to the atomic bomb.

[10] Albert Einstein, 1905. See reference 2.

But let's return to absolute space and time. Einstein made two incredible postulates about the nature of physical reality:

- Absolute uniform motion cannot be detected.
- The speed of light is independent of the motion of the source.

These postulates reconcile mechanics and electro magnetism, at the expense of mechanics, and they neatly explain the Michelson-Morley result. There is no fringe shift because light travels with the same speed $c = 3 \times 10^8$ m/s along both arms of the apparatus no matter how they are oriented. Since the motion of the source does not affect the speed of light, this also means that there is no need for an ether.

c) Length contraction and time dilation.

Three direct consequences of Einstein's postulates are:

- The speed of light is always the value c in any frame of reference (x, y, z axes) that is moving with a constant speed (an inertial frame).
- If your are standing still on the surface of the Earth, an object of length L moving past you with a speed of v will have a length as measured by you of

$$L' = L \left(1 - v^2/c^2\right)^{1/2},$$

- In addition, a clock moving past you with a speed v will tick more slowly that an identical clock on you body:

$$T' = T / \left(1 - v^2/c^2\right)^{1/2}.$$

Moving lengths contract in their direction of motion, and moving clocks run slowly.

2.   The death of absolute time.

We consider a thought experiment used to determine the "now" for a person using simultaneous events. The scenario involves lighting strikes occurring at two points on a railroad track exactly the same distance from the position of a person standing beside a track. The light from these two strikes reaches the person at the same time, and that instant is the person's definition of "NOW."

A train is passing exactly as this happens, and a woman on the train at a window just opposite the position of the person on the ground also sees the lightning strikes, and they make marks on the train. The women is positioned on the train exactly between these marks. Consider what the women traveler sees:

As the traveller is moving toward the flash at the right, she moves toward the flash 2 and it reaches her before the flash 1. The flashes originate form spots initially the same distance from her on the train as proven by the scorch marks on the train. So she concludes that the two flashes did not occur at simultaneously, and she cannot define the reception of the light as defining her "NOW." The flashes are not simultaneous from the point of view of the traveler because she believes Einstein who said that light always moves with the speed c. If the flashes reach her at different times and they are the same distance apart, then they cannot be simultaneous.

The temporal sequence of events is relative – time is not absolute; time is relative.

3.	Relativistic mechanics.

a) A limit on the speed of massive objects.

When we discussed Newton's second law, we mentioned that he assumed space and time to be absolute and independent. He then introduced the idea of accelerated motion due to unbalance forces, and produced his second law

$$F = M\,a = M\,\Delta v/\Delta t,$$

where M is the mass of an object moving with a velocity v and with an acceleration a. We later introduce the concept of momentum

$$P = M\,v,$$

and remarked that Newton's law can be expressed as

$$F = M\,\Delta(P/M)/\Delta t = \Delta P/\Delta t.$$

This is merely an algebraic manipulation if M is constant. However, that change in mechanics than we mentioned Einstein needed to make to mechanics consistent with Maxwell's electromagnetic theory is that mass in not constant. In fact, if an object moves with a speed v, its mass becomes

$$M = M_o/\,(1 - v^2/c^2)^{1/2}.$$

Here, M_o is the mass of the object measured when it is at rest. Thus, the mass of an object increases as it moves, and it increases without bound as the speed of the object approaches the speed of light. This means that an object with a rest mass cannot move faster than the speed of light.

b) Mass and energy.

Now, the change in mechanics that Einstein demanded is to take the momentum form of Newton's second law as the correct form:

$$F = \Delta P / \Delta t,$$
$$P = M_o \, v \, / \, (1 - v^2/c^2)^{1/2}$$

We can work with this form of the second law just as we did earlier in the course, and when the energy concept is presented, it turns out that the energy of a mass M moving with a speed v becomes

$$E = M \, c^2 = M_o / \, (1 - v^2/c^2)^{1/2} \, c^2 = M_o \, c^2 + M_o \, v^2.$$

The remarkable conclusion is that energy is related to the relativistic mass of the object. Mass is energy, and mass energy can be converted to other forms of energy like heat. The last form of the above equation holds when the speed of the object is not close to light speed, but it is interesting. It says that the energy of a mass is the sum of its kinetic energy and the quantity $M_o \, c^2$. An object has energy by virtue of its rest mass.

So, if the rest mass of an object can become reduced as a nuclear reaction (as happens within with uranium core of a nuclear reactor) rest-mass energy will be converted to heat. As an example, suppose that one milligram of uranium mass is converted to energy:

$$\Delta E = MC^2 = 1 \times 10^{-6} \, kg \, (3 \times 10^{8} \, m/s)^2$$
$$= 9 \times 10^{10} \, joules.$$

A ton of TNT releases 4.2×10^9 joules.

So

1 milligram of mass $\iff$ 21.4 tons of TNT

When paradigms of reality change, a worldview is not all that is affected. We have just witnessed what Einstein's special theory of relativity wrought:

- Space in not absolute. There is no ether.
- Time is not absolute. Time is subjective and observer dependent.
- Space and time are related through Einstein's equations connecting inertial frames of reference. The general theory of relativity was presented by Einstein in 1916, and it connects space, time and matter – see reference 7.
- Mass is energy and its conversion can produce huge amounts of energy of other forms.

CHAPTER 16

The World View Changes – Quantum Mechanics

1.   The first signs of trouble.

a) Black-body radiation.

Consider an oven whose interior is heated to high temperature. The hot walls of the oven radiate EM waves of many frequencies (strong in the infrared). A small hole in one of the walls is used to measure the intensity of the radiation (energy per unit area) over the spectrum of wavelengths. This simple observation led a staggering surprise.

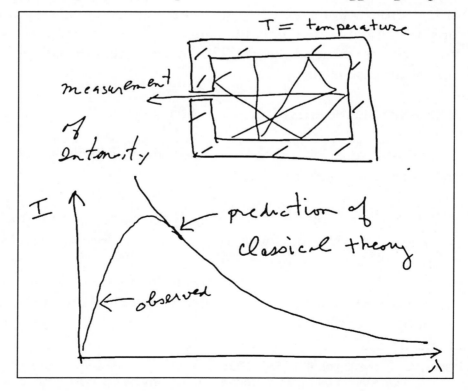

Classical physics predicts that the intensity should increase without bound for small wavelengths of the radiation in the oven. The observation is that the intensity actually drops to zero as the wavelength decreases.

The explanation that Max Planck[11] gave in the year 1901 is that the energy of the radiation is not continuous. It is discrete in pieces or quanta of h f, where f is the frequency and h is a constant named "the planck constant:"

$$h = 6.63 \times 10^{-23} \text{ joules. second.}$$

b) Atomic spectra.

If light from a hot gas such as hydrogen of mercury is viewed using a prism of diffraction grating, the light is seen to break up into discrete colors characteristic of the gas. This indicates that the energy levels of the gas are discrete or quantized.

c) The photoelectric effect (Einstein, 1905)[12].

If light is incident on a metallic surface, electrons will be ejected from the surface. This electric current:

- Only depends on the wavelength of the light, not on its intensity.
- The flow of current will be zero until a specific wavelength is reached. As the energy content of EM radiation increases as wavelength decreases, this means that there is a maximum wavelength (or minimum energy) required to produce the photoelectric current.

---

[11] Max Planck, Ann. Physik, vol. 4, p. 553, 1901.
[12] Albert Einstein working in that patent office came up with the Special Theory of Relativity, an atomic explanation for Brownian motion, and an explanation of the photoelectric effect. The latter appears in: Ann. Physik, vol. 17, p. 355, 1905. He won the Nobel prize in Physics for his explanation of the photoelectric effect.

- These data are not explained by the physics of pre-1905.
- Einstein's explanation:

Assumption: light is composed of particles that carry an energy

$$E_{photon} = hf,$$

where

$$h = \text{Planck's constant}$$
$$= 6.63 \times 10^{-34} \text{ joules} \cdot \text{sec}$$

Energy balance :

$$\text{Energy in} = hf = \text{Energy out}$$
$$= K + W$$
$$K = \frac{1}{2} m_e v_e^2 \text{ (kinetic energy)}$$
$$W = \text{constant characteristic of the metal.}$$

d) Example 1.

What is the kinetic energy of the most energetic electron emitted when light of wavelength 410 nm (violet) illuminates a sodium surface whose work function W = 2.28 electron volts (eV).

- The electron volt as a unit of energy:

  1 eV = energy acquired by an electron when it is accelerate by a voltage difference of 1 volt

  $$= e\, V = 1.602 \times 10^{-19} \text{ C (1 volt)}$$
  $$= 1.602 \times 10^{-19} \text{ joules.}$$

- Solution:

$$h f = k + W$$

$$h f = 6.63 \times 10^{-34} \text{ joule} \cdot \text{sec } (f)$$

$$f = \frac{c}{\lambda} = \frac{3 \times 10^{8} \text{ m/s}}{410 \times 10^{-9} \text{ m}} = 7.32 \times 10^{14} \text{ Hz}$$

$$\rightarrow h f = 6.63 \times 10^{-34} \text{ J} \cdot \text{s} \left(7.32 \times 10^{14} \text{ s}^{-1} \right)$$

$$= 4.85 \times 10^{-19} \text{ joule} \frac{1 eV}{1.602 \times 10^{-19} \text{ J}}$$

$$= 3.03 \, eV$$

$$\rightarrow k = \underline{h f - W = 3.03 \, eV - 2.28 \, eV}$$

$$\boxed{= 0.75 \, eV}$$

e) Example 2.

What is the energy of a "red or 700 nm" photon? What is the energy of a "blue or 400 nm" photon?

Red $\lambda = 700 \text{ nm}$

$$E = h f = \frac{hc}{\lambda} = \frac{6.63 \times 10^{-34} \text{ J} \cdot \text{s } 3 \times 10^{8} \text{ m/s}}{700 \times 10^{-9} \text{ m}}$$

$$= 2.84 \times 11^{-19} \text{ J} \frac{eV}{1.602 \times 10^{19} \text{ J}}$$

$$\boxed{= 1.77 \, eV}$$

Blue

$$E = 1.77 \, eV \left(\frac{700}{400} \right) \boxed{= 3.1 \, eV}$$

2. Mysteries about the universe today.

- 90% of the matter in the universe is not composed of the stuff that we know (photons, electrons, quarks (protons and neutons),....). This mysterious stuff produces a gravitational field (has mass) but does not interact in any other way with ordinary matter. It is called "dark matter."
- Of the remaining 10%, about 8/10 is energy involved in making the universe accelerate. It is called "dark energy." It can be accounted for by using a modification of Einstein's general theory of gravitation and an attached term called the cosmological constant. We called this term his greatest mistake, but it now seems to give a mechanism for the acceleration of the universe.

3. Particles and Waves.

a) Atomic Spectra explained by Bohr (1912).

We observed in class that the light from hot gases such as hydrogen, mercury vapor and sodium emit a discrete spectrum of light. For example, hydrogen emits two colors in the visible spectrum, red and blue, in addition to an ultraviolet component. Classical physics has no explanation.

Schrödinger[13] and the Copenhagen[14] school came up with an explanation that associates a wave nature to a particle, in particular the electron in the hydrogen atom. Effectively, the possible orbits of the election around the proton nucleus are standing waves:

---

[13] Erwin Schrödinger, Ann. Physik, vol.79, p. 361, 1926. His work is involves an equation that can be used to evaluate the particle wave. Eisenberg developed quantum mechanics using a different approach, and received the Nobel Prize for this work in 1932, a year before Schrödinger's prize which he shared with Maurice P.A.M. Dirac.

[14] Werner Heisenberg, Zeitschrift fur Physik, vol. 33, p. 879, 1925.

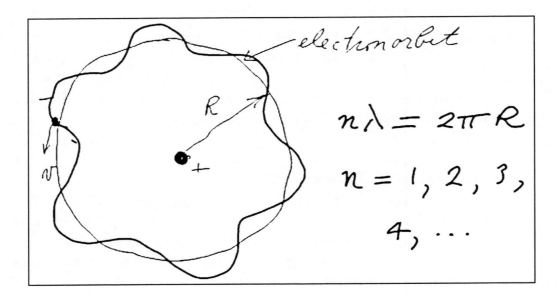

b) The particle wavelength.

What is this wavelength associated with an electron? Louis de Broglie[15] (1924) theorized that it is associated with the momentum of the electron as

$$P = momentum = m\,v = h\,/\,\lambda.$$

When we discussed light, it was mentioned that if the wavelength is much smaller that the size of obstacles through which the light moves, then the light can be considered to move as rays – straight paths much like a particle. When the wavelength is comparable to the obstacles, then the wave nature is important and one gets characteristic wave effects like interference (bright and dark fringes). The "de Broglie" wavelength of particles behaves in a similar way.

• The wavelength of a mass of 0.2 g moving at a speed of 100 m/s.

$$P = m\,v = \frac{h}{\lambda}$$
$$\lambda = \frac{h}{m\,v} = \frac{6.63\times10^{-34}\,j\cdot a}{.2\times10^{-3}kg\,(100\,m/s)} = 3.31\times10^{-35}\,m$$

---

[15] The papers reference above rest on the particle-wave assumption of Louis de Broglie published in Phil. Mag. Vol. 47, p 446, 1924.

- An electron moving at a speed of 5×10^6 m/s.

$$\lambda = \frac{h}{mv} = \frac{6.63 \times 10^{-34} \, J \cdot s}{9.11 \times 10^{-31} kg \, (5 \times 10^6 \, s)} = 1.46 \times 10^{-10} \, m$$

$$\rightarrow \text{atomic size}$$

- The double –slit experiment for a single electron moving toward a powered aluminum target with atomic spacing, d = 8.62×10^{-10} m. The resulting interference pattern looks like that formed by light incident on double slits, and the angle to the first bright fringe is: angle = λ/d = 1.46×10^{-10} m/ 8.62×10^{-10} m = 0.169 radians = 9.7 degrees. This looks very much like a diffraction experiment using light.

c) The energy levels of hydrogen.

Putting all these rather eclectic parts together along with some classical physics, we get an energy-level spectrum:

$$F_e = \frac{ke^2}{R^2} = \frac{mv^2}{R}$$

$$E = \text{energy of electron}$$

$$= U + K$$

$$= -\frac{ke^2}{2R}$$

gives Bohr's[16] formula for the energies and the orbital radius of the hydrogen atom:

$$E_n = - me^4/(8\varepsilon_0^2 h^2)\ 1/n^2, n = 1, 2, 3, 4, \ldots,$$
$$= - 13.6\ eV/n^2,$$
$$R_n = n^2\ (5.29 \times 10^{-11})\ m.$$

d) Verification

The spectral lines are neated explained by the Bohr model and its evaluation of the energy levels for hydrogen and the evaluation of the spectral lines.
It is first instructive to calculate photon energies in electron volts and at associate them with wavelengths:

$h = 6.63 \times 10^{-34}$ joules seconds $(1\ eV/1.602 \times 10^{-19}\ j) = 4.14 \times 10^{-15}$ eV seconds.
$\Delta E =$ energy of photon $= h\ f = h\ c\ /\ \lambda = 12.4 \times 10^{-7}$ eV meters$/\lambda = 1240$ eV nm$/\lambda$.

So, for example we can calculate the energies associated with photons in the visible spectral range:

$$\lambda(red) = 600\ nm => \Delta E = 1240/600\ eV = 2.1\ eV,$$

$$\lambda(blue) = 400\ nm => \Delta E = 1240/400\ eV = 3.1\ eV.$$

---

[16] Niels Bohr is the father of quantum mechanics as the patron of the Copenhagen school, and the inventor of a crude model for the atom that in effect simply postulated discrete energy states based on Planck's assumption: Phil. Mag., vol, 26, p. 1, 1913.

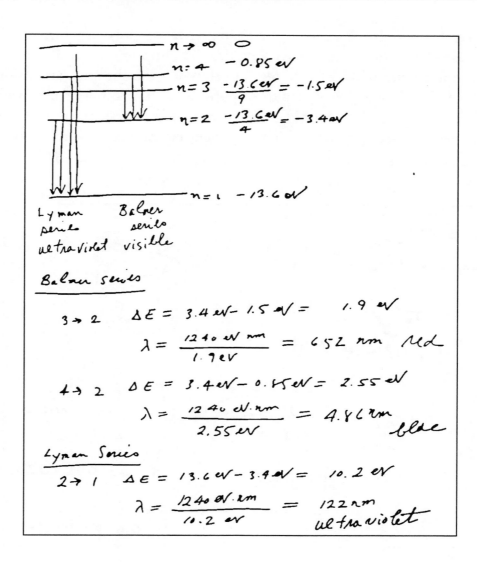

This agrees exactly with our observations and with precise measurements.

4. Probability Waves and the uncertainty principle[17].

a) Wave interference and comparison with light

When we discussed light, it was mentioned that if the wavelength is much smaller that the size of obstacles through which the light moves, then the light can be considered to move as rays – straight

---

[17] Heisenberg's 1925 paper is in reference 3.

paths much like a particle. When the wavelength is comparable to the obstacles, then the wave nature is important and one gets characteristic wave effects like interference (bright and dark fringes). The "De Broglie" wavelength of particles behaves in a similar way.

We have described an experiment using a double-slit arrangement to prove the wave nature of light. A electron moves toward a powered aluminum target with atomic spacing, $d = 8.62 \times 10^{-10}$ m. The resulting pattern on a screen is depicted below:

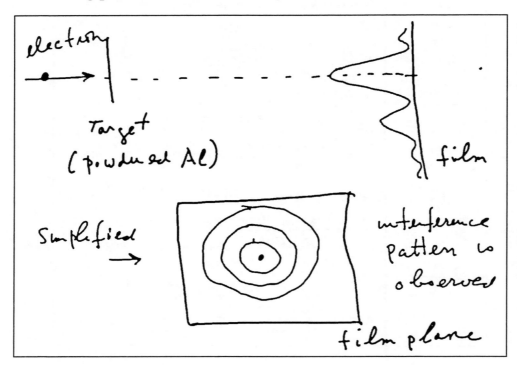

The interference pattern formed by such electrons scattered from aluminum powered and x-rays scattered by randomly oriented crystals are the same.

Let's analyze this by replacing the powered aluminum by a double slit. The resulting interference pattern would look like that formed by light incident on double slits, and the angle to the first bright fringe is:

angle $= \lambda / d = 1.46 \times 10^{-10}$ m/ 8.62×10^{-10} m $= 0.169$ radians $= 9.7$ degrees.

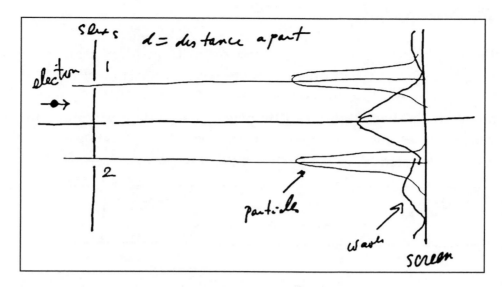

The distance to the first "bright" fringe is $\Delta x = 1.46 \times 10^{-10}$ m $(10m)/\ 8.62 \times 0^{-10}m = 1.69$ m.

b) The probability wave.[18]

The pattern shown above is interpreted as a probability that the election will fall at certain spots of the screen. The most likely spot is the center, the least likely spots are at the "dark fringe" spots, and the more likely spots are located at the "bright fringe" spots.

- This probability pattern will be seen for a beam of electrons or for one electron. But, in order to see it, the electron cannot be observed as it moves from the slits to the screen.
- If the electron is traced, it will move either through the top slit or bottom slit (not both), and it will fall in two clumps on the screen just as if we were shooting bullets trough the two slits.
- If the electron were to be only very gently traced, that part which is seen moving through either slit would look like bullets, and that part that is not seen would look like the interference of light.

---

[18] The particle wave in interpreted as a probability amplitude (its square is a probability). This curious idea was introduced by Max Born in 1926, at the very beginning of the invention of the quantum theory: M. Born, Z. Physik, vol. 37, p. 863 (1926); Nature, vol. 119, p. 354 (1927). Thus, the calculations of physics about physical realities become the evaluation of experimental probabilities. This is the way things stand today after nearly eighty years of testing in all experimental applications in the "quantum domain."

c) A particle in a box.

Let us place a particle like an electron in a one-dimensional box of length L so that it can only be found some where between x = 0 and x = L. Let the box be atomic size so L = 1 × 10^{-10} m. Just as we analyzed the hydrogen atom by placing a standing wave in an orbit, we represent the electron inside the box as a standing wave. The wave is denoted Ψ, as is the custom, and we define Pr = $|\Psi|^2$.

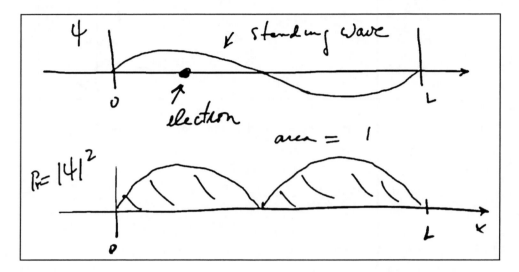

The wave represents the particle in such a way that it square is the probability of the particle being at some location. The bottom curve represents the probability of the particle in the box being somewhere inside the box, and the area under the curve is equal to 1 – the particle is somewhere inside the box. The particle has zero probability of being at x = 0, x = L/2 and at x = L. It has maximum probability of being located either at x = L/4 or x = 3L/4. A measurement of the particle could find it on the left side of the box. A second measurement could find it on the right side of the box. But it goes from the left to the right without moving through the center.

d) Impact of the uncertainty principle.

The momentum of the electron is p = mv = h/λ. The standing wave shown has a wavelength λ = twice the distance between nodes = L, so

$$p = h/L \rightarrow p\, L = h.$$

Now, the electron is somewhere inside the box, so the uncertainty in its position is $\Delta x = L$, the momentum of the electron. As momentum is a vector quantity, it can be directed either to the right or the left, so the uncertainty in the momentum is $\Delta p = p - (-p) = 2p$. Therefore,

$$p \, L = \Delta p/2 \; \Delta x = h \rightarrow \Delta p \; \Delta x = h/2.$$

Along with Einstein's theory of relativity, this is one of the most revolutionary ideas in twentieth-century physics. It is called the Heisenberg uncertainty principle:

$$\Delta p \; \Delta x > h.$$

This is a statement about the limits of knowledge about particles in nature. If a particle is located precisely so that there is no uncertainly in its position, i.e. $\Delta x = 0$, then its momentum or speed in entirely unknown, ie. $\Delta p \rightarrow$ infinity. Conversely, if the speed of the particle in known with absolute precision, then its position cannot be determined. **This is not a statement about our inability to make accurate measurements. It is a statement about the limits of knowledge.** The uncertainty principle is a direct result of the wave nature of particles.

More importantly, the new worldview changes because of the uncertainty principle. It says that reality is not described by the kind of pictures that Newton or Einstein used to envision the interplay of matter in space-time. It says that we can only know the results of experiments with certain probabilities. The idea of something moving under in time under the influence of forces is replaced by techniques for calculating the results of observations. Reality is defined by experimental results, and these are usually not definite – the theoretical structure gives us probabilities for outcomes. Einstein was not amused by this state of affairs, and he spent the rest of his life trying to find a way to preserve the existence of an objective reality mirrored rather than replaced by the processes of measurement.

One consequence of the uncertainly principal is that an electron cannot be brought to rest at a point in space. For example, what is the uncertainty in location of a proton when its speed is 0.1% the speed of the speed of light?

Proton : $m = 1.67 \times 10^{-27} kg$

$v = (0.001) \, 3 \times 10^{4} \, m/s = 3 \times 10^{5} \, m/s$

$P = 1.67 \times 10^{-27} kg \, (3 \times 10^{5} \, m/s)$

$= 5.01 \times 10^{-22} \, kg \, m/s$

$\Delta P = 0.01 \, P = 5 \times 10^{-24} \, kg \, m/s$

$\Delta P \, \Delta x \geq h$

$\rightarrow \Delta x \geq \dfrac{h}{\Delta P} = \dfrac{6.63 \times 10^{-34} \, J \cdot sec}{5 \times 10^{-24} \, kg \, m/sec}$

$= 1.32 \times 10^{-10} \, m$

5. The superposition of possible states.

a) Return to the particle in a box.

We again consider the situation where a particle like an electron resides in a one-dimensional box of length L. The particle cannot exist outside the box. The possible states as standing waves within the box are shown below:

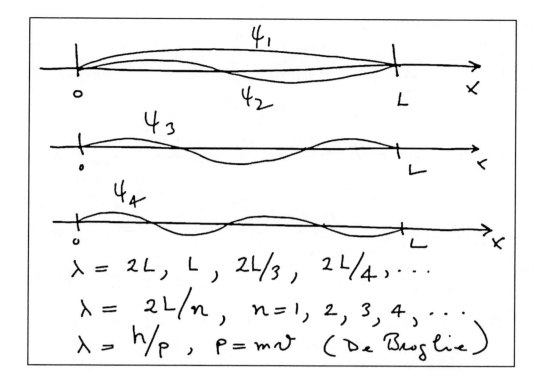

$$\lambda = 2L, \ L, \ 2L/3, \ 2L/4, \ldots$$

$$\lambda = 2L/n, \quad n = 1, 2, 3, 4, \ldots$$

$$\lambda = h/p, \quad p = m\nu \quad (\text{De Broglie})$$

b) The general state of the particle in the box.

The general state is found by superimposing the "harmonic" components as

$$\psi = \psi_1 + \psi_2 + \psi_3 + \psi_4 + \ldots.$$

This is exactly the way we treated the general form of a wave on a string, and the general physical shape of that observed wave was indeed this superposition – a photograph would show a complex pattern found by adding the harmonic components.

In quantum mechanic the square of the above wave represents a probability, not something that can be photographed, and the measurement of the state of the particle will always be **one** of the component waves- never more than one. Each of these possible realizations has an energy that we can calculate.

c) The energy levels of a particle in a one-dimensional box.

$$\lambda = \frac{2L}{n}, \quad n = 1, 2, 3, \cdots$$

$$\lambda = \frac{h}{P}, \quad P = m v$$

$$E = K = \tfrac{1}{2} m v^2 = \tfrac{1}{2} m \left(\frac{P}{m}\right)^2 = \frac{P^2}{2m}$$

$$= \frac{1}{2m}\left(\frac{h}{\lambda}\right)^2 = \frac{1}{2m}\left(\frac{h}{2L/n}\right)^2$$

$$\boxed{E = \frac{h^2}{4m L^2}\, n^2, \quad n = 1, 2, 3, \cdots}$$

This is the result one obtains by using the Schrödinger equation – the quantum-mechanical law of motion. Note that the energy levels do not include zero energy.

---

6.   Playing dice with the universe.

The general state of a system is represented by a probability wave ψ, and it is built up of many component states that represent possible realizations or alternate realities for that state:

$$\psi = \psi_1 + \psi_2 + \psi_3 + \psi_4 + \cdots$$

A measurement of this state will result in one of these realizations popping into existence. Which realization will occur is not known beforehand, but the theory tells us how to calculate the probability for it to happen.

a) First a word about probabilities

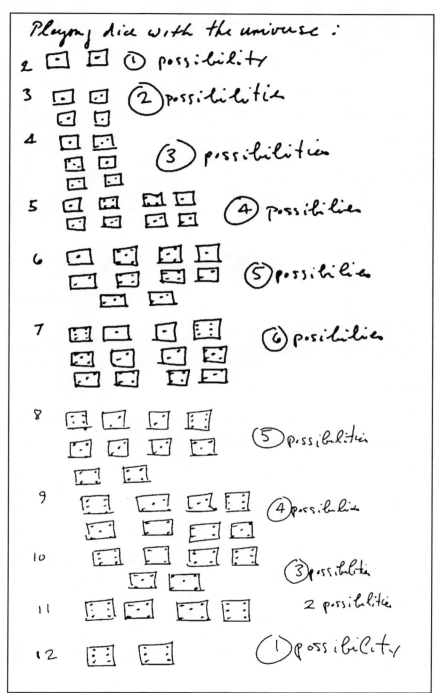

The total number of possibilities is 1+2+3+4+5+6+5+4+3+2 c+1 = 36. The probability of rolling a seven is 6/36 = 0.167 and the probability of rolling a 2 is 1/36 = 0.0276. The probability of rolling a 4 then rolling a 4 again is (3/36)×(3/36) = .0069.

---

7.   The state of a system and alternate realities.

The state of a system is a wave whose square is a probability. If the state is represented by ψ, it is constructed by adding together its possible realizations:

$$\psi = \psi_1 + \psi_2 + \psi_3 + \psi_4 + \ldots$$

When the state is observed, it pops into one of these realizations with the probability $|\psi_i|^2$, where I = 1, 2, 3, … .

We will consider a number of examples to illustrate this idea.

a) The particle in a box formed from components to make a ramp.

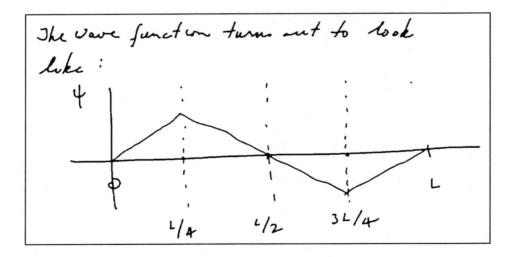

The probability wave is $|\psi|^2$, and it looks like:

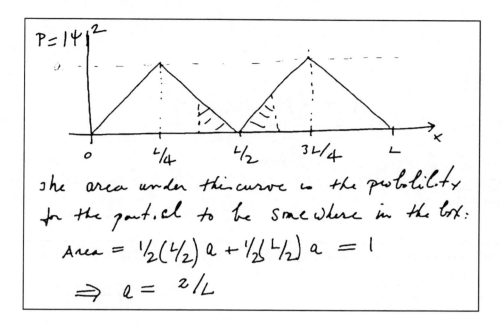

$P = |\psi|^2$

$o \qquad L/4 \qquad L/2 \qquad 3L/4 \qquad L$

The area under the curve is the probability for the particle to be somewhere in the box:

Area $= \frac{1}{2}\left(\frac{L}{2}\right)a + \frac{1}{2}\left(\frac{L}{2}\right)a = 1$

$\Rightarrow a = 2/L$

What is the probability that the particle will be somewhere between x = 3L/8 and x = 5L/8?

Probability = area under the P vs x curve between x = 3L/8 and 5L/8

$= \frac{1}{2}\left(\frac{L}{8}\right)\left(\frac{a}{2}\right) + \frac{1}{2}\left(\frac{L}{8}\right)\left(\frac{a}{2}\right)$

$= \frac{L}{16}a = \frac{L}{16}\cdot\frac{2}{L} = \frac{2}{8}$

$= 0.25$

b) The wave packet.

The following is a Maple program to add "harmonic waves" corresponding to a small range of momenta to get a wave function in space:

> restart;xx:=6*x/Pi;y:=(x,k)-> cos(k*x);

$$xx := \frac{6\,x}{\pi}$$

$$y := (x,\, k) \rightarrow \cos(k\,x)$$

>   wp:=x-
>0.25*y(x,9)+0.3333*y(x,10)+0.5*y(x,11)+y(x,12)+0.5*y(x,13)+0.3333*y(x,1
4)+0.25*y(x,15);

$$wp := x \rightarrow 0.25\,y(x,\,9) + 0.3333\,y(x,\,10) + 0.5\,y(x,\,11) + y(x,\,12) + 0.5\,y(x,\,13) + 0.3333\,y(x,\,14)$$
$$+ 0.25\,y(x,\,15)$$

> plot(wp(x),x=1..11,`wavepactket`=-5..5);

The "wp" is a state wave function composed of seven wave corresponding to different momenta. These are $p = 9\,h/(2\pi)$ to $p = 15\,h/(2\pi)$, so the spread in the values of p is $\Delta p = 6\,h/(2\pi)$

The sum of these harmonic waves is the probability wave in space, and we see that it is localized about x = 6 with a spread of about $\Delta x = 4$:

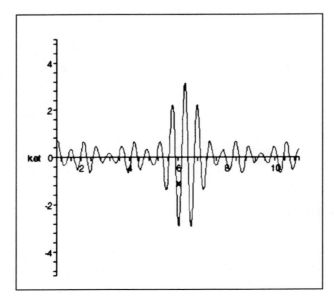

The product $\Delta p \, \Delta x = [6 \, h/(2\pi)] \, 4 = 24 \, h/12 = 2 \, h$, and this is consistent with the Heisenberg uncertainty principle.

c) Cartoon states

$$\psi = \psi_{a1,b1,c1,d1} + \psi_{a2,b2,c2,d2} + \psi_{a3,b3,c3,d3} + \psi_{a4,b4,c4,d4}$$

Here, the parameters a, b, c and d represent characteristics of the system ψ and each of these characteristic can have four values. A measurement of the system produces the system in a state where these values take on one, and only one, of their allowed values:

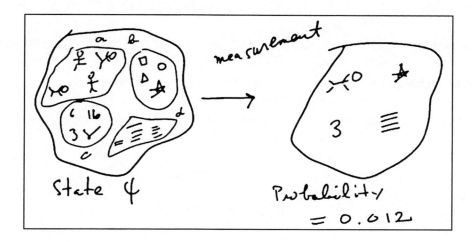

This is, of course, a cartoon of the situation, but it brings out the salient features:

- The state wave function of a system is composed of component waves that correspond to actual realizations of the system.
- The square of the state wave function gives the probabilities of each of these realizations, and the sum of all the probabilities is 1.0.
- When the system is observed, it becomes one of the component realizations. One does not know beforehand which will occur, but quantum theory computes the probabilities for each realization to occur.

d) Another cartoon using dice to compute the probability

The state of a character called Root Canal has six characteristics: hair color, eye color, height, weight, character and attitude. The each of these characteristics has a probability of 1/6, and each individual characteristic has possible values that are determined by a toss of dice:

Hair color: brown (3, 0.0555), red (6, 0.1389), gray (7, 0.1667), black(all others,0.6389);

Eye color: hazel (5, 0.1111), green (8, 0.1389), blue (4,0.0833), brown (all other tosses, 0.6667);

Height: 5'2" (5, 0.1111), 6'1" (11, 0.0555), 4'8" (12, 0.0278), 5'8" (all others, 0.8056);

Weight: 120 lbs (9, 0.1111), 150 lbs (2, 0.0278), 200 lbs (12, 0.0278), 250 lbs(all others, 0.8333);

Character: nice (7, 0.1667), nasty (9, 0.1111), Charming (8, 0.1389), aloof (all others, 0.5834);

Attitude: lazy (9, 0.1111), enthusiastic (8, 0.1389), irritating (6, 0.1389), positive (all others, 0.6111).

Recall that the probabilities of the possible tosses are: (2, 1/36 = 0.0278), (3, 2/36 = 0.0555), (4, 3/36 = 0.0833), (5, 4/36 = 0.1111), (6, 5/36 = 0.1389), (7, 6/36 = 0.1667), (8, 5/360.1389), (9, 4/36 = 0.1111), (10, 3/36 = 0.0833), (11, 2/36 = 0.0555), (12, 1/36 = 0.0278).

The most probable outcome is for Root Canal to have: black hair, brown eyes, weigh 250 lbs, be aloof but positive. The probability for this outcome is

1/6 (.6389+.6667+.8056+.8333+.5834+.6111) = 0.6898

Let's throw the dice to see what the laws of quantum probabilities give:

Toss

#	1	6	→	red hair	unlikely
	2	8	→	green eyes	unlikely
	3	12	→	4' 8"	unlikely
	4	3	→	250 lbs	most likely
	5	4	→	aloof	most likely
	6	10	→	positive	most likely

Probability for this realization

$$= \frac{1}{6}(.1563 + .1389 + .0274 + .8333$$
$$+ .5834 + .6111) = .3918$$

APPENDIX

A. The Arrow of Time

Time in classical physics is absolute and independent of space, but the equations of Newtonian mechanics contains the time parameter "t" that can just as easily move to smaller values (the past) as to larger values (the future). The film can run in reverse. However, the second law of thermodynamics tells us that closed systems will change in the direction of more likely states or increasing disorder, and this gives a direction to time. Even when there is a movement toward increasing complexity, like the emergence of life, the net effect on the universe is toward increasing disorder or increasing entropy.

The class in the first course created projects that illustrate this idea of a direction to time – the arrow of time. Six samples are shown here.

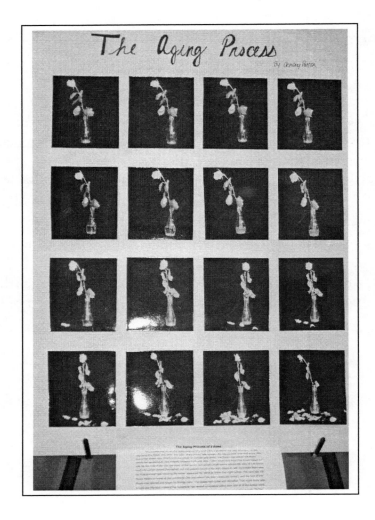

Ashley Patton shows the aging process through photographs of a rose in a vase. The end result is the expected dead and dried out specimen. Several students followed this theme, but Ashley's pictures are strikingly rendered in a progression of black and white photos carefully positioned over the three or four days that takes the living and beautiful rose to a heap of dead and dried pedals.

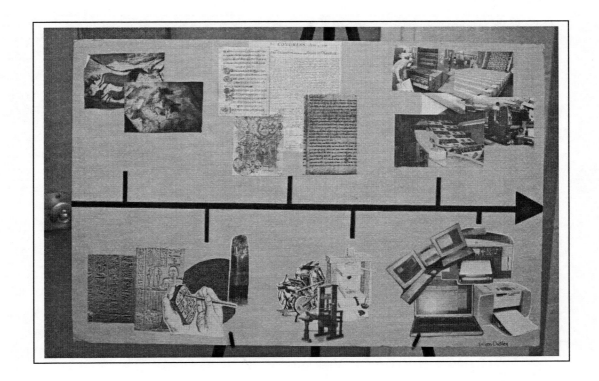

Maxime Iattoni takes an interesting view of the arrow of time in communication, and this time is tracing the art of communication from cave drawings, to stone tablets, to language on parchment and onward to the computer. This is a trail of decreasing entropy — from vague order to highly complex order. The interesting aspect of the arrow of time is that although incredible complexity is the result of emergence of complexity, the overall effect is toward a loss of useful energy. Although the end of the story is assured by the second law of thermodynamics, the story unfolds in unexpected and surprising ways.

Jamunia Rosner shows the cycle of life using pictures of her relatives — the cycle from pregnancy, birth, childhood, adulthood, old age and death. The cycle is shown as a circle, which can go around any number of times.

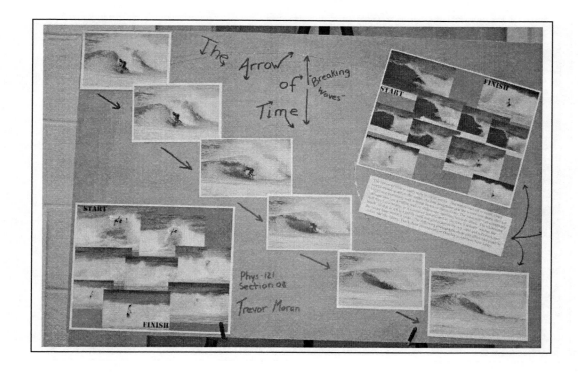

Trevor Moran has chosen an excellent example of the pent up and highly organized energy being released into a relaxed state. The breaking of waves is a beautiful way to show the flow of entropy in the natural flow of water.

Juntine Brining, a Graphic Design student, shows the moment as it stands poised between the future and the past. Watches each showing a different version of "now," a splash at its maximum, a breaking class and a sand dune as it will never be again.

Kaki Jervis is a Fashion Designer, and she has an interesting evolution of the poncho. It is one of the examples of the arrow of time in which the rising or falling of entropy is unclear, but the modern look does less complex.

B.	Alternate Realities

The discussion of the quantum state as a superposition of possibilities has given rise to many artistic fantasies. Like the recent movie "Run Lola Run" in which a young couple relive events that are possible life scenarios with wildly different outcomes- from utter tragedy to a happy ending. All the members of the class took the tools of their disciplines to investigate this idea, and five are presented here. To facilitate the presentation in this appendix, photographs, drawings or collages were chosen, but there were others equally interesting projects in the forms of sound clips, movies, poetry, papers and dramatic presentations.

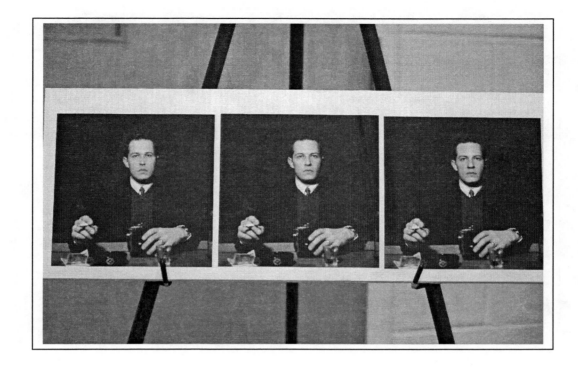

This picture is an example of alternate realities created by photographer Sarah Stolfa, photography major and an experienced and recognized photographer. The photo in the center is the subject, as he exists, the photo on the left contains a skillful splicing of his left eye occupying both sides. The photo on the right has two right eyes joined. The person does indeed look unworldly in the two outside views, as no one is perfectly symmetrical.

Jessica Hetzl depicts Alice in her wonderland with unreal players who occupy the Lewis Carroll world.

Bradley Breneisen has gathered several images of the great horn player Miles Davis. The top is a fairly realistic drawing of Mr. Davis, the second a more stylized cartoon-like rendition. The third is not of this world, but it captures the essence of the musician's multicolored and unique music with powerful colors that stand forward for the listener take or leave

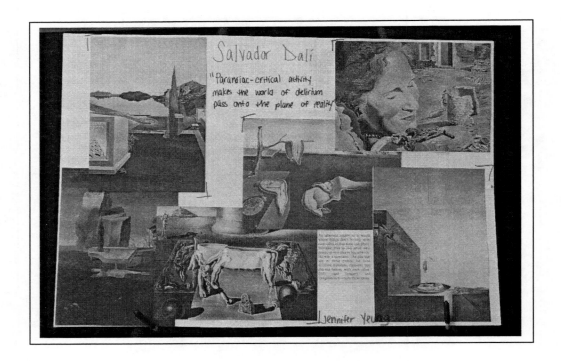

Jennifer Yeung collected these images from Salvador Dali, who was a masterful creator of a world that is not like anything possible in a physics state. However, his fantastic creations contains statements about reality that some find profound and moving and upsetting. He even took a direct shot at quantum mechanics and the uncertainty principle in his "nuclear" phase.

Deniz Bilgatay presents a pictorial array of recent films whose themes are alternate realities. So we see The Matrix, The Butterfly Effect, Run Lola Run, the Minority Report, the Planet of the Apes and others. All of these depict worlds plausibly close to the one we know, but with bizarre differences that stretch our imaginations.

Adam Nguyen, a major in Digital Media, designed this interplay of colors and imbedded figures in his own interpretation of alternate realities.